JUNIOR SONGS

HOLLIS DANN, Mus. D.

PROFESSOR OF MUSIC, AND HEAD OF DEPARTMENT OF MUSIC
AT CORNELL UNIVERSITY
AUTHOR OF THE HOLLIS DANN MUSIC COURSE

AMERICAN BOOK COMPANY
NEW YORK   CINCINNATI   CHICAGO
BOSTON   ATLANTA

PREFACE

This book is designed to furnish attractive and appropriate song material for use in all schools where changing voices introduce peculiar problems. To meet this situation a large amount of the material has been specially composed or arranged, with optional parts for changed voices.

The special treatment thus demanded has resulted in the division of the book into five parts, each of which, with the exception of Part Five, contributes to the solution of the problem of voice distribution.

PART ONE—All of the songs in Part One are for unchanged voices, in unison, two, or three parts, some with and some without piano accompaniment. In many cases the accompaniment is optional. In order to provide music the pitch and range of which are precisely suited to fulfill the conditions of this section, most of the material has been composed or arranged specially for this book. A high musical quality together with technical (vocal) fitness has thus been successfully attained.

PART TWO—This section comprises four-part songs for unchanged voices and bass. The boys' part, however, is optional, and all of the songs may be sung in three parts, the effect when so sung being complete and thoroughly musical. Thus the first section of the book is supplemented by more than fifty pages of material available in classes where the boys' voices have not yet changed. The bass part utilizes only the limited register that may with safety be employed at this period of the youth's singing experience. In this section are included also a few special unison songs which may be sung by all voices. About two-thirds of the songs have piano accompaniments; the rest are unaccompanied part-songs.

PART THREE—This section consists essentially of four-part songs, but it differs from Part Two in that the bass voice is essential to the completion of the harmony. As in the other sections, a considerable number of piano accompaniments are included. In addition to the four-part material, there are a few carefully selected bass songs to be sung by a solo voice or by all the boys in unison, but in no case has the safe and easy baritone register been overstepped either above or below. These boys' songs usually have four-part Refrains which not only lend variety but also serve to hold the interest of the class as a whole.

PART FOUR—The songs in this section, whether with or without piano accompaniment, are written or arranged generally for three parts — two unchanged voices and bass. There are also some selections in which the bass is optional. As in Part Three, many songs comprise melodies to be sung *ad libitum* by a solo voice, the three-part Refrain to be taken by the full class. Here again, all the selections, whether composed for this book or specially arranged, lie within the most favorable registers of the various voices, so that development may proceed normally and without the possibility of vocal strain.

PART FIVE—This section is devoted to Community Songs and Hymns and has been included because of the widespread demand for songs which express popular community spirit. The selections used have been chosen because they have contributed to an unusual degree to the development of national feeling.

No uniform type of arrangement has been adopted, but where new arrangements have been made, each song is presented in that form to which it seems musically best adapted. With regard to Community Songs it may be said that, with few exceptions, no authentic accompaniments are in existence, none having been written by the composers of the melodies. Such accompaniments as have been supplied from time to time and have passed current in different song collections are so palpably inferior to the melodies that rewriting rather than revision seemed inevitable. The accompaniments herein provided are simple, straightforward, and musicianly. All curious or unusual harmonies as well as every other suggestion of artificiality have been avoided as contrary to the genius of Folk Music.

The injudicious use of the changing voice often results in irreparable injury to the mature voice. The boy soprano gradually loses his upper tones so that he sings easily only in the second soprano or first alto. Nor should he be encouraged to sing low tones until his speaking voice as well as his singing voice shows the deeper and heavier quality of maturity. In other words, the singing voice should follow, not anticipate, nature's lead. Likewise, one of the least understood features of the adolescent problem is the changing voice of the girl. As in the case of the boy, a disinclination to sing the upper tones is the first evidence of the approaching change. Here also the utmost care must be exercised to protect the changing voice.

The large problem then at this period is the relation of voice conditions to the character and compass of the music used; and it is this problem that has been given first consideration in the preparation of Junior Songs.

Acknowledgments are due to The Youth's Companion for the privilege of using " Ho, Heave Ho!" "The Night Song," "A Summer Garden," and "A Merry Race"; to the Century Company for "The Land Without a Name"; and to Arthur Edward Johnstone for "Salute to the Flag," "Flag of Flags," and "Alma Mater."

PART ONE

UNCHANGED VOICES
SOPRANO, SECOND SOPRANO, AND ALTO

SUNRISE

HARVEY WORTHINGTON LOOMIS

ARTHUR EDWARD JOHNSTONE

1. Wid - er and still more wide The gates of the morn - ing swing;
2. Mar-shalled from east and west, The hosts of the dawn sweep by,
3. O'er the ho - ri - zon's rim, Be - yond the ea - gle's flight,

Clear - er and e'er more clear The notes of the for - est birds ring; The
Garbed in the light of day— A pa - geant ad - vanc - ing on high— In
Lanc - es of gold ap - pear, To van - quish the sin - is - ter night. The

earth, the sea, the clouds, the sky, Have cho - sen the sun for their king.
daz - zling white, they throng the blue, To wel - come the lord of the sky.
day is born! The sun is here! He floods all the world with his light.

PIPPA'S SONG

Robert Browning

John E. West

Con moto moderato ♩ = 104

The year's at the spring, And day's at the morn; Morning's at seven; The hill-side's dew-pearled; The lark's on the wing; The snail's on the thorn; God's in his

(piano) morn; . . Morning's at seven; The hill-side's dew-pearled; The lark's on the wing; The snail's on the thorn; . . . . . .

THE LINDEN TREE

FRANZ SCHUBERT
Three-part arr.

Tranquillo ♩ = 80

1. A - bove the vil - lage foun - tain   A lin - den spreads a shade; How
2. To - night I breathe its per - fume   And think of long a - go, And
3. And once, when win - try north - winds   Swept down from out the sky   To

oft be - neath its branch - es   My fan - cies fond have played!   It
close my eyes, re - mem - b'ring   The days I used to know.   Be -
bar my toil - ing foot - steps   And twist my cloak a - wry,   In

bears the carved in - i - tials   Of man - y a girl and boy;   It seemed a trust - y
neath the lin - den's ver - dure   A warmth of wel - come glows;   Its leaves are soft - ly
dreams of home - sick yearn - ing   I saw my lin - den tree   And seemed to hear it

com - rade   To share   my pain or joy,   To share   my pain or joy.
whis - p'ring, "Come close   and find   re - pose,   Come close   and find re - pose!"
call me, "Come home,   I'll shel - ter thee,   Come home,   I'll shel - ter thee!"

BENDEMEER'S STREAM

Thomas Moore

Old Tune

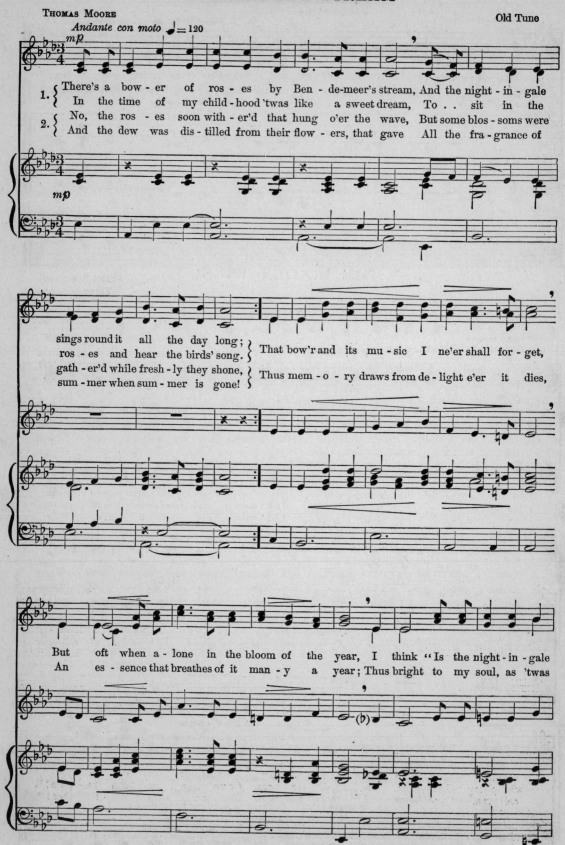

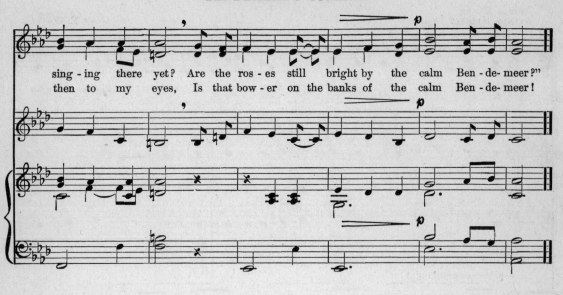

sing - ing there yet? Are the ros - es still bright by the calm Ben - de- meer?"
then to my eyes, Is that bow - er on the banks of the calm Ben - de- meer!

THOSE EVENING BELLS

THOMAS MOORE

HARVEY WORTHINGTON LOOMIS

Andantino ♪ = 132

1. Those eve - ning bells! those eve - ning bells! How man - y a tale their
2. Those joy - ous hours have passed a - way; And man - y a heart, that
3, And so 'twill be when I am gone; That tune - ful peal will

mu - sic tells, Of youth, and home, and that sweet time When
then was gay, With - in the tomb now dark - ly dwells, And
still ring on, While oth - er bards shall walk these dells, And

rall.   a tempo

last . I heard their sooth - - ing chime. . . . .
hears no more those eve - - ning bells. . . . .
sing your praise, sweet eve - - ning bells! . . . .

(Sweet eve - ning bells.)

rall.   a tempo

SUMMER CLOUDS

Nathan Haskell Dole

John E. West

Andante con moto ♩ = 72

1. High a - bove us slow - ly sail - ing, Lit - tle clouds so soft and
2. When the sum - mer sun is shin - ing, And the sky is blue a -

1. High a - bove us slow - ly sail - ing, Lit - tle clouds so soft and
2. When the sum - mer sun is shin - ing, And the sky is blue a -

(For rehearsal only)

white, You are like .. the wings of
bove, Then you look .. at us and

white, You are like .. the wings of an - gels, ... Watch - ing
bove, Then you look .. at us and send us ..... Ra - diant

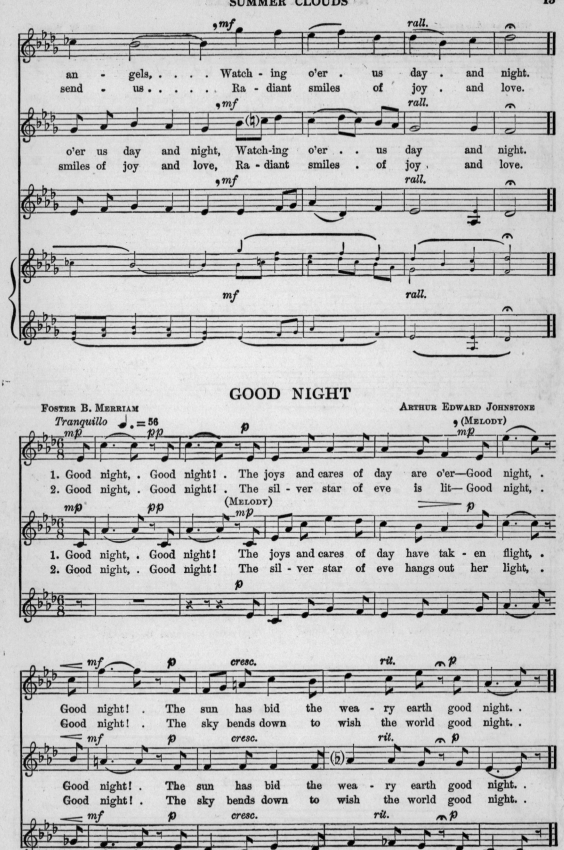

GOOD NIGHT

FOSTER B. MERRIAM

ARTHUR EDWARD JOHNSTONE

ROBIN REDBREAST

WILLIAM ALLINGHAM

E. W. JOHNS

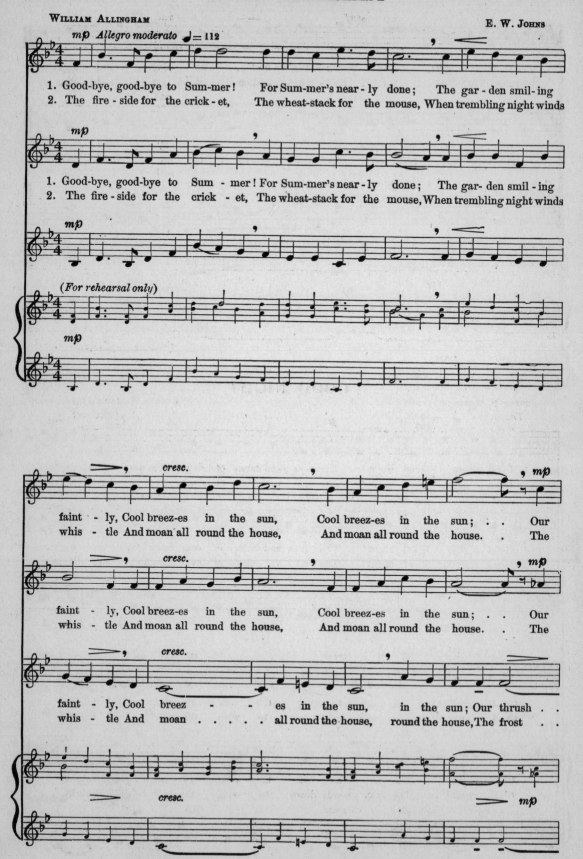

1. Good-bye, good-bye to Sum-mer! For Sum-mer's near-ly done; The gar-den smil-ing
2. The fire-side for the crick-et, The wheat-stack for the mouse, When trembling night winds

1. Good-bye, good-bye to Sum-mer! For Sum-mer's near-ly done; The gar-den smil-ing
2. The fire-side for the crick-et, The wheat-stack for the mouse, When trembling night winds

(For rehearsal only)

faint - ly, Cool breez-es in the sun, Cool breez-es in the sun; .. Our
whis - tle And moan all round the house, And moan all round the house. . The

faint - ly, Cool breez-es in the sun, Cool breez-es in the sun; .. Our
whis - tle And moan all round the house, And moan all round the house. . The

faint - ly, Cool breez - - es in the sun, in the sun; Our thrush ..
whis - tle And moan . . . . . all round the house, round the house, The frost ..

thrush - es now are si - lent, Our swal - lows flown a - way, But Rob - in's here in
frost - y ways like i - ron, The branch - es plum'd with snow, A - las! . in win - ter

thrush - es now are si - lent, Our swal - lows flown a - way, But Rob - in's here in
frost - y ways like i - ron, The branch - es plum'd with snow, A - las! in win - ter

. . es now are si - lent, Our swal - lows flown a - way, But Rob - in's here in
. . y ways like i - ron, The branch - es plum'd with snow, A - las! in win - ter

coat of brown And scar - let breast-knot gay. O Rob - in, O
dead and dark, Where can poor Rob - in go? O Rob - in, O

coat of brown And scar - let breast-knot gay. O Rob - in, O
dead and dark, Where can poor Rob - in go? O Rob - in, O

coat of brown And scar - let breast-knot gay. O Rob - in, O
dead and dark, Where can poor Rob - in go? O Rob - in, O

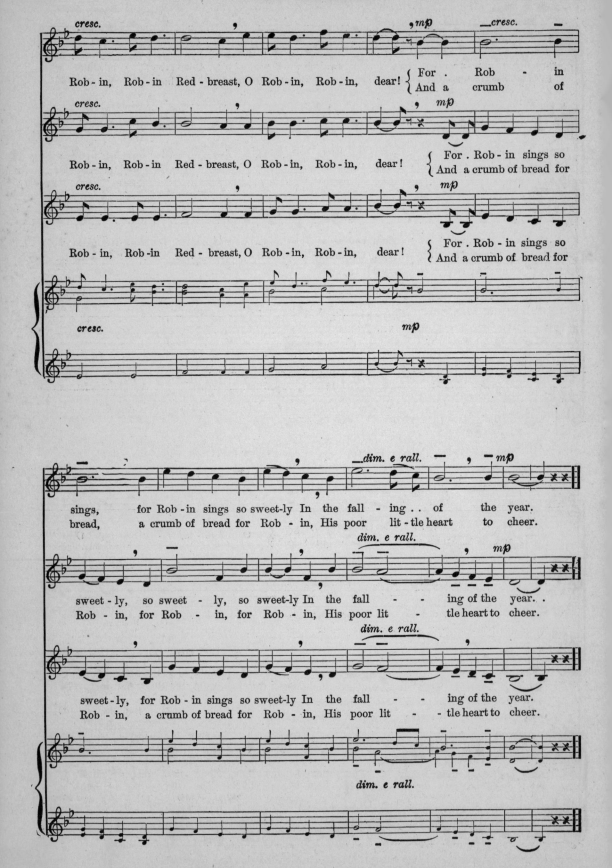

JOHN B. TABB

FRANZ ABT

Moderato ♩ = 104

1. 'Tis Christ-mas night, the pure snow a flock un-num-bered lies: The old Ju-de-an
2. A mys-t'ry deep-er still folds the won-d'ring hosts of light, Till, lo, with ho-ly

flocks a-glow keep watch with-in the skies. An i-cy still-ness
rev-'rence pale, that dims each di-a-dem, The lord-liest earth-ward

clos-er holds The puls-es of the breathless night, And all the Christmas night, The
bend-ing, hail The liv-ing light of Beth-le-hem, Glad Bethlehem's liv-ing light, The

an-gel stars shine bright For Beth-lehem's light, For Beth-lehem's light.
ho-ly Christ-mas light, Glad Beth-lehem's light, The liv-ing light.

HO, HEAVE HO!

B. M. WATERS
From " The Youth's Companion "

E. W. JOHNS

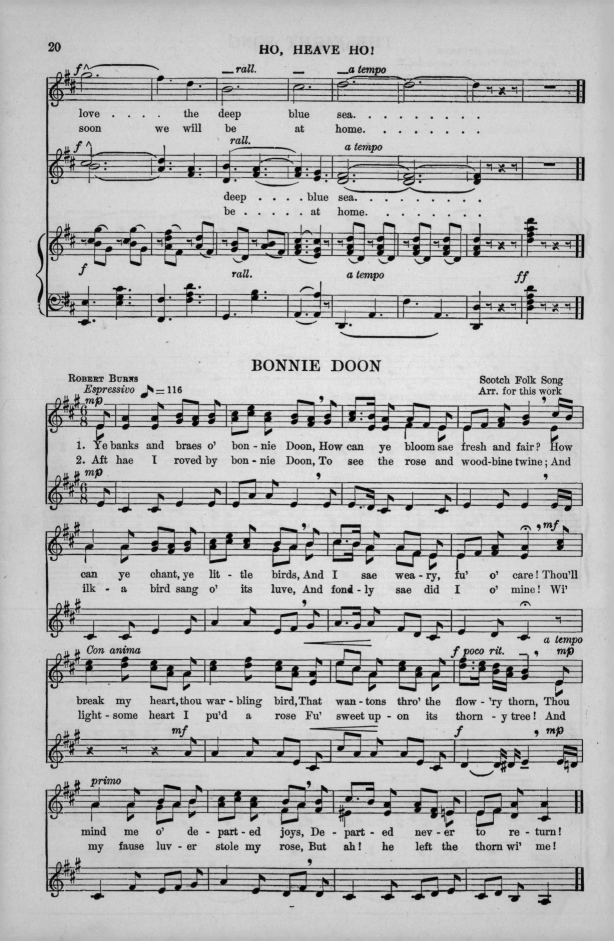

love . . . . the deep blue sea. . . . .
soon we will be at home. . . . .

deep . . . . blue sea. . . . .
be . . . . . at home. . . . .

BONNIE DOON

ROBERT BURNS
Espressivo ♪ = 116

Scotch Folk Song
Arr. for this work

1. Ye banks and braes o' bon-nie Doon, How can ye bloom sae fresh and fair? How
2. Aft hae I roved by bon-nie Doon, To see the rose and wood-bine twine; And

can ye chant, ye lit-tle birds, And I sae wea-ry, fu' o' care! Thou'll
ilk-a bird sang o' its luve, And fond-ly sae did I o' mine! Wi'

break my heart, thou war-bling bird, That wan-tons thro' the flow-'ry thorn, Thou
light-some heart I pu'd a rose Fu' sweet up-on its thorn-y tree! And

mind me o' de-part-ed joys, De-part-ed nev-er to re-turn!
my fause luv-er stole my rose, But ah! he left the thorn wi' me!

bors   too   soon."

Tempo Primo mp

And the   lit - tle bird flew   to   the top of the tree,   And looked

up . . .   in - to the   sky. . .   "Our   time . .   for sing - ing is

short," quoth he, . . . "And sing in the night will I." . . . . Ah, . . .

. . ah, ah, ... ah, . . . ah, ah, . . ah, ah, . . ah, . .

Ah, . . . ah, ah, ... ah, . . . ah, ah, . . ah,

. . ah, ah, ... ah, . . . ah, ah!. . . . . . .

ah, . . ah, . . ah, ah, ... ah, ah! . . . .

LIFT THINE EYES

Felix Mendelssohn-Bartholdy
From the oratorio, "Elijah"

never, will never slumber, never slumber, ber,

slum- ber, nev- er, will nev- er slum- ber,

slum ber, nev- er, will nev- er slum- ber, will nev - er slum- ber,

Lift thine eyes, O lift thine eyes to the moun-tains, whence com-eth, whence com-eth, whence

Lift thine eyes, O lift thine eyes . to the moun-tains, whence com-eth, whence com-eth, whence

Lift thine eyes, O lift thine eyes to the moun-tains, whence .. com-eth, whence

com - eth help, whence com-eth, whence com-eth, whence com-eth help.

com - eth help, whence com - eth, whence com-eth, whence com-eth help.

AT DAYBREAK

Allegro moderato ♩ = 120   Two-part Canon   Arthur Edward Johnstone

Wake with songs of glad-ness To words of love and cheer;

Dull care .. and ev-'ry thought of sad - ness

With shades of night dis-ap-pear, For the day-break is here.

THE BLOSSOM

WILLIAM BLAKE
From "Songs of Innocence"

JOHN E. WEST

Allegretto ♩ = 88

1. Mer - ry, mer - ry spar - - - row! Un - der leaves so green A hap - py
2. Pret - ty, pret - ty rob - - - in! Un - der leaves so green A hap - py

Mer - ry, mer - ry spar - row! Un - der leaves so green A hap - py
Pret - ty, pret - ty rob - in! Un - der leaves so green A hap - py

blos - som Sees you, swift as ar - row, Seek your cradle nar - row, Near my bos - om.
blos - som Hears you, sob - bing, sob - bing, Pret - ty, pret - ty rob - in, Near my bos - om.

LEAD, KINDLY LIGHT

JOHN HENRY NEWMAN

JOHN B. DYKES
Three-part arr.

Moderato ♩ = 66

1. Lead, kind - ly Light! a - mid th' en - cir - cling gloom, . Lead thou me on; . The night is
2. I was not ev - er thus, nor pray'd that thou . Shouldst lead me on; . I lov'd to
3. So long thy pow'r has blest me, sure it still . . Will lead me on . O'er moor and

dark, and I am far from home, . . Lead thou me on; . . Keep thou my feet; I
choose and see my path; but now . . . Lead thou me on; . . I lov'd the gar - ish
fen, o'er crag and tor - rent till . . . The night is gone; . And with the morn those

do not ask to see . . The dis - tant scene; one step e - nough for me.
day; and, spite of fears, . Pride ruled my will: re - mem - ber not . past years.
an - gel fac - es smile . Which I have lov'd long since, and lost . a - while.

THE LAND WITHOUT A NAME

Helen Gray Cone
From "St. Nicholas"

E. W. Johns

Allegro giusto ♩ = 100

1. Where the Sun sails bold on the Sea of Gold Past the Vio - let . Is - lands fair; And the rag - ged shapes of the Ros - y Capes And the Cas - tles of the Air, Can you call a - right all that coun - try bright That is washed by waves like flame? 'Tis the coast ad-mired, 'tis the clime de - sired, Of the Land with - out . . . a Name.

2. And the way to go, if you fain would know, Is to char - ter the Cres - cent Ship, All of sil - ver, pale, with a cob - web sail, And . mer - ri - ly does she dip! There's a crew of Hopes at her film - y ropes, And on board that Ship of Fame . . Man-y a long - ing dream seeks the shore a - gleam, Of the Land with - out . . . a Name.

THISTLE-DOWN

Clara Doty Bates

John E. West

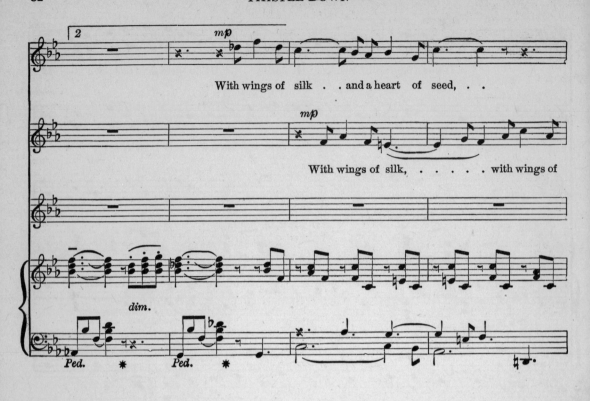

With wings of silk . . and a heart of seed, . .

With wings of silk, ... with wings of

silk . . and a heart of seed, . . With wings of silk . and a heart . . of seed, O - ver

With wings of silk, ... With wings of silk . . and a heart of seed, . .   O - ver

O - ver field and town . . It sails, . . o - ver field and town . It

field and town . It sails, . . O - ver field and town . . It sails, . . it

field and town . It sails, . . O - ver field and town . . It sails, . . it

sails, . . . Ah! . . . . quaint lit - tle bird in - deed . Is the

sails, . . . Ah! . . . . quaint lit - tle bird in - deed . Is] the

sails, . . . Ah! . . . . quaint lit - tle bird in - deed . Is the

Ped. ✻ Ped. ✻ Ped. ✻ Ped. ✻ Ped. ✻

THE NIGHT HAS A THOUSAND EYES

Francis W. Bourdillon

E. W. Johns

A SUMMER GARDEN

From "The Youth's Companion"

JOHN E. WEST

A SUMMER GARDEN

Andante tranquillo   *dim. e rit.*   **pp**

three lit - tle girls . . . . were fast a - sleep. . . . .

p   *rit.*   **pp**

And three lit - tle girls . . . . were fast a - sleep. .

p   *rit.*   **pp**

And three lit - tle girls . . . . were fast a - sleep. .

Andante tranquillo

p   *rit.*   **pp**

O WORSHIP THE KING

Sir ROBERT GRANT   JOSEF HAYDN

Allegro moderato ♩ = 112

mf

1. O wor - ship the King all glo - rious a - bove; O grate - ful - ly
2. O tell of his might, O sing of his grace, Whose robe is the
3. Frail chil - dren of dust, and fee - ble as frail, In thee do we

mf

mp

sing his power and his love; Our Shield and De - fend - er, the
light; whose can - o - py space; His char - iots of wrath the deep
trust, nor find thee to fail; Thy mer - cies how ten - der, how

mp

f

An - cient of Days, Pa - vil - ion'd in splen - dor, and gird - ed with praise.
thun - der clouds form, And dark is his path on the wings of the storm.
firm to the end, Our Mak - er, De - fend - er, Re - deem - er, and Friend.

f

Mary Felicia Butts
From "Wide Awake"

John E. West

THE SHEPHERD

William Blake
From " Songs of Innocence "

John E. West

How sweet is the shep - herd's sweet lot! . . . . From the

How sweet is the shep - - - herd's sweet lot! From the

How sweet is the shep - herd's sweet lot! . . . . . . From the

(For rehearsal only)

morn to the eve - ning he strays; . . . . He shall fol - low his sheep, his

morn to the eve - - - ning he strays; He shall fol - - low his

morn to the eve - ning he strays; . . . . He shall fol - - - low his

I WOULD THAT MY LOVE

HEINRICH HEINE

FELIX MENDELSSOHN-BARTHOLDY

while they held their hands out - stretched, . To catch the di - a-monds

But while they held their hands out-stretched,

gay, . . the di - a-monds gay, . . A mil - lion lit - tle sun-beams came And

To catch the di - a-monds gay, . . A mil - lion lit - tle

stole them all a - way, and stole them all . . . . a -

sun-beams came, And stole them all a - way, and stole them all . . . a -

Ped.

MASSA'S IN DE COLD, COLD GROUND

Stephen C. Foster

Stephen C. Foster

With sentiment ♩ = 80

A MAY FROST

Harvey Worthington Loomis

Felix Mendelssohn-Bartholdy
Three-part arr.

Un poco Allegro ♩ = 116

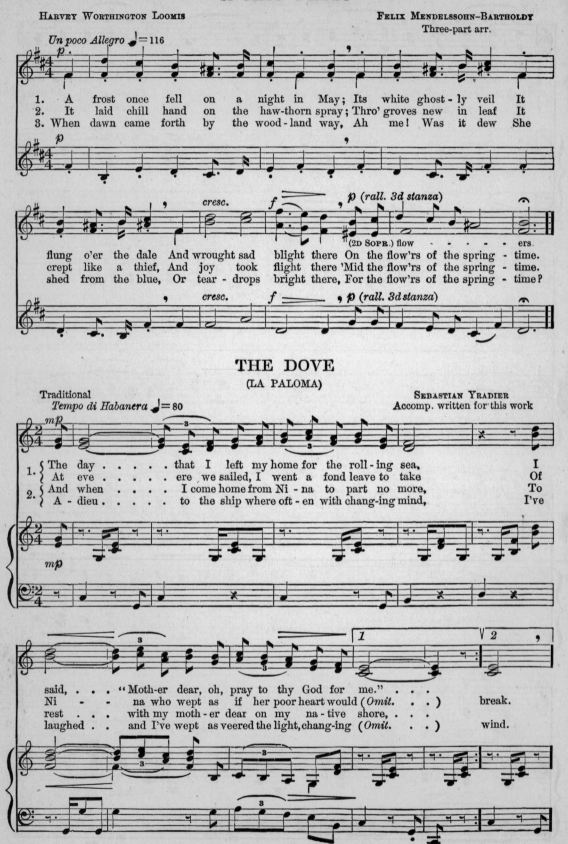

1. A frost once fell on a night in May; Its white ghost-ly veil It
2. It laid chill hand on the haw-thorn spray; Thro' groves new in leaf It
3. When dawn came forth by the wood-land way, Ah me! Was it dew She

cresc. *f* *p (rall. 3d stanza)*
(2D Sopr.) flow - - - - ers.

flung o'er the dale And wrought sad blight there On the flow'rs of the spring - time.
crept like a thief, And joy took flight there 'Mid the flow'rs of the spring - time.
shed from the blue, Or tear - drops bright there, For the flow'rs of the spring - time?

THE DOVE
(LA PALOMA)

Traditional
Tempo di Habanera ♩ = 80

Sebastian Yradier
Accomp. written for this work

1. { The day . . . . . that I left my home for the roll - ing sea,   I
     { At eve . . . . . ere we sailed, I went a fond leave to take   Of
2. { And when . . . . I come home from Ni - na to part no more,   To
     { A - dieu . . . . . to the ship where oft - en with chang-ing mind,   I've

said, . . . "Moth-er dear, oh, pray to thy God for me." . . .
Ni - - na who wept as if her poor heart would (*Omit.* . .) break.
rest . . . with my moth - er dear on my na - tive shore, . . .
laughed . . and I've wept as veered the light, chang-ing (*Omit.* . .) wind.

Ni - na, if I should die and o'er o-cean's foam . . . Soft - ly a white dove
O - pen thy lat - tice, dear - est, for it will be . . . . My faith- ful soul that
Then comes the day, the hap - py and bless-ed day . . . Chas-ing all sad-ness,
Ni - na so fair, all smiles, will be by my side, . . . Ni - na, so dear, will

on a fair eve should come; . . .
lov-ing comes back to (*Omit . . .*) thee!
sor-row and care a - way; Oh, a life on the sea,
be my own blush-ing (*Omit . . .*) bride.

Sing - ing joy - ous and free! Ah! . . . . we are go - ing,

None are so gay as we. we. . . . . . .

A MERRY RACE

RACHEL GEDDES SMITH
From "The Youth's Companion"

JOHN E. WEST

1. A laugh - ing band of
2. For six long years they

1. A laugh - ing band of
2. For six long years they

1. A laugh - ing band of
2. For six long years they

lit - tle waves Went gai - ly out to sea, ... For Moth - er O - cean
rip - pled on, And nev - er stopp'd to rest. ... They gen - tly rock'd the

lit - tle waves Went gai - ly out to sea, ... For Moth - er O - cean
rip - pled on, And nev - er stopp'd to rest. ... They gen - tly rock'd the

lit - tle waves Went gai - ly out to sea, ... For Moth - er O - cean
rip - pled on, And nev - er stopp'd to rest. ... They gen - tly rock'd the

call'd to them—   "Come chil - dren, come to
man - y ships   On Moth - er O - cean's

called to them—   "Come chil - dren, come to   me,   come to
man - y ships   On Moth - er O - cean's breast,   O - cean's

called to them—   "Come chil - dren, come to   me, ...   Come chil - dren, come to
man - y ships   On Moth - er O - cean's   breast, . . .   On Moth - er O - cean's

Ped.   Ped.   Ped.   Ped.   Ped.   Ped.   Ped.

me." . .   They   all   put   on   their
breast. . .   When   all   at once   they

me." . . .
breast. . .

me." . . .   They
breast. . .   When

Ped.   Ped.   Ped.   Ped.

OUR BOYS

Harvey Worthington Loomis   (Complete without Bass)   Arthur Edward Johnstone

In march tempo

1. Thou-sands are has - ten - ing toward the square To view the great pa - rade; .
2. Pass - ing the gaud - y re - view - ing stand, And thro' the flo - ral arch, .

All of the hol - i- day throng are there, In gay ap-par- el ar - rayed; . The flags are proud-ly
Gal-lant pro-tec-tors of sea and land, Ten thousand soldiers a - march, Where flute and fife are

fly - ing, The crowds "Hurrah!" are cry - ing; With martial tread the reg - i- ments come, To
play - ing, And trum-pet loud - ly bray - ing Be-neath the Red, the Blue and the White, In

beat of the drum—No heart is glum, But puls - es bound At thrill - ing sound Of the
u - ni- form bright, A splen - did sight! While hearts keep time To meas - ured rime Of the

tramp, tramp, tramp, tramp. Wel - come the boys, hip, hip, hur - rah!

tramp, tramp, tramp, tramp. Tramp, tramp, tramp, tramp,

Wak - en the air with a might - y huz - za! Firm, bold, march-ing a - long,

tramp, tramp, tramp, tramp, tramp, tramp, tramp, tramp,

Sci - ons of Free - dom, young and strong! . . . .

tramp, tramp, tramp, tramp, tramp, tramp, tramp, tramp,

* May be sung by basses

Know-ing that Might is born of Right. Hail, hail, Pride of the Land!

tramp, tramp, tramp, tramp, tramp, tramp, tramp, tramp,

Brave lads, for Lib-er-ty's cause they stand! Hip, hur-rah! . . .

tramp, tramp, tramp, tramp, tramp; Hip, hur-rah! . . .

A PAGEANT

JENNIE W. SUTTON

ARTHUR EDWARD JOHNSTONE

Tempo di marcia ♩ = 104

1. { Great throngs mass-ing Where reg-i-ments are pass-ing; The bu-gles have
   { Vast our cho-rus, The skies of az-ure o'er us; We cel-e-brate

2. { High hearts beat-ing! The he-ro le-gions meet-ing In bat-tle-worn
   { Linked for-ev-er, No fate the tie shall sev-er, U-nit-ing for

waked ere the morn; Ral - lied from the high-way, Ral - lied from the
glo - ry and fame; Now a might - y na - tion, Thrilled with ju - bi -
kha - ki ar - rayed! Cheer our no - ble free-men, Sol - dier - lads and
Truth, heart and hand; Gold - en chimes are ring - ing, Mul - ti - tudes are

by - way, An ar - my no foe dare scorn!
la - tion Is voic - ing its grand ac - claim.
sea - men; The fame of them ne'er shall fade!
sing - ing, To hon - or our own dear land.

REFRAIN

Home of In - de - pen - dence, Land of Free-dom's birth, The light of your re -

splen - dence .. Il - lumes the earth. Wav - ing flags ap - pear .. In all their

PART TWO

UNCHANGED VOICES
WITH OPTIONAL BASS

SALUTE TO THE FLAG

Arthur Edward Johnstone

I pledge al - le-giance to . my flag, and to the Re-pub - lic for which it stands;

One na - tion, in - di - vis - i - ble, with lib - er - ty and jus - tice for

all, with lib - er - ty and jus - tice for all. . .

FLAG OF FLAGS

Harvey Worthington Loomis

Arthur Edward Johnstone

Tempo di marcia ♩ = 120

1. Hail to thee! Hail to thee! Stand-ard a-bove, Flag that we love:
Hail to thee! Hail to thee! Flow'r of the sky, Bloom-ing on high,
2. Hail to thee! Hail to thee! High in the blue, Flag of the true,
Hail to thee! Hail to thee! Staunch as a star Shin-ing a-far,

All the glo - ry Of Free-dom's sto - ry, From out thy folds un - furl - ing.
Dawn-light ten - der And sun - set splen-dor Thy ra - diant hues em - pearl - ing.
Faith un - bound-ed On thee is found-ed, As loy - al hearts ac - claim thee.
Trib - ute glow-ing On thee be - stow-ing, The Flag of Flags we name thee.

Refrain

Flash the watch-word, "Might with Right!" O-ver hill and dale and moun-tain-height, As the

count - less years shall roll. Truth dwells in thy col - ors three,

Youth and age sing a - like to thee The song of a na - tion's soul.

HOMELAND
(COMPLETE WITHOUT BASS)

GEO. W. PENNINGTON

Old Tune
Harmonized for this work

Vigoroso ♩ = 112

1. Out where the prai - rie reach - es Bound - less and free,
2. Out 'mid the snow - clad moun - tains Fain would I be;
3. Out in the Land of Sun - set Edged by the sea,

My home - land, my

home - land is call - ing e'er to.. me, . My home - land, my

home - land is call - ing e'er to me. call - ing e'er to me.

WINTER CARNIVAL

(COMPLETE WITHOUT BASS)

KATHARINE WHITMORE

Danish Folk Dance
Three-part arr.

1. { Good mor - row, good mor - row, Ye danc - ers one and all, } With ev - 'ry - one jol - ly A -
No sor - row, no sor - row Shall lurk with - in this hall.

2. { Of laugh - ter, of laugh - ter And joy we take our fill, } While cou - ples are swing - ing And
Then aft - er, then aft - er Each Jack may find his Jill.

twin - ing the hol - ly Bid in - no - cent Fol - ly Ap - pear at our call. Good mor - row, good
car - il - lons ring - ing And mo - ments are wing - ing We dance with a will. Then aft - er, then

mor - row, Ye danc - ers one and all.
aft - er, Each Jack may find his Jill.

Light we trip a - round, fa - la - la! Gay the fid - dles

Fid - dles are sound - ing, Gay ech - oes re -

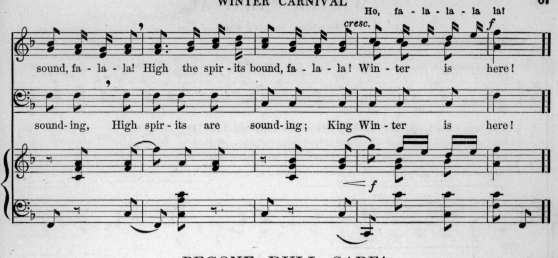

Ho, fa - la - la - la - la!
cresc.
f

sound, fa - la - la! High the spir - its bound, fa - la - la! Win - ter is here!

sound-ing, High spir - its are sound-ing; King Win - ter is here!

BEGONE, DULL CARE!

Traditional (COMPLETE WITHOUT BASS) Old English
Three-part arr.

Vivace ♩. = 88

1. Be - gone, dull care! . . I prith - ee be - gone from me! . .
2. Oh, too much care . . Will make a young man turn gray; .

(Both stanzas) Be - gone, . . . dull care! Be - gone! .

Be - gone, dull care! You and I . shall nev - er a - gree. .
And too much care . . . Will turn an old man to clay. .

I prith - ee be - gone, dull care! I prith - ee be - gone, be - gone, dull care!

poco rit.

Long time hast thou been tar - rying here And fain . thou wouldst me kill, . .
My wife shall dance, and I will sing, So mer - ri - ly pass the day, . .

poco rit.

a tempo

But i' faith, . dull . . . care, . . . Thou nev - er shalt have thy will. .
For I hold it one of the wis - est things To drive dull care a - way. ,

Dull care,
'Tis wise

O NO, JOHN!

Somerset Folk Song
Accomp. by Arthur Edward Johnstone

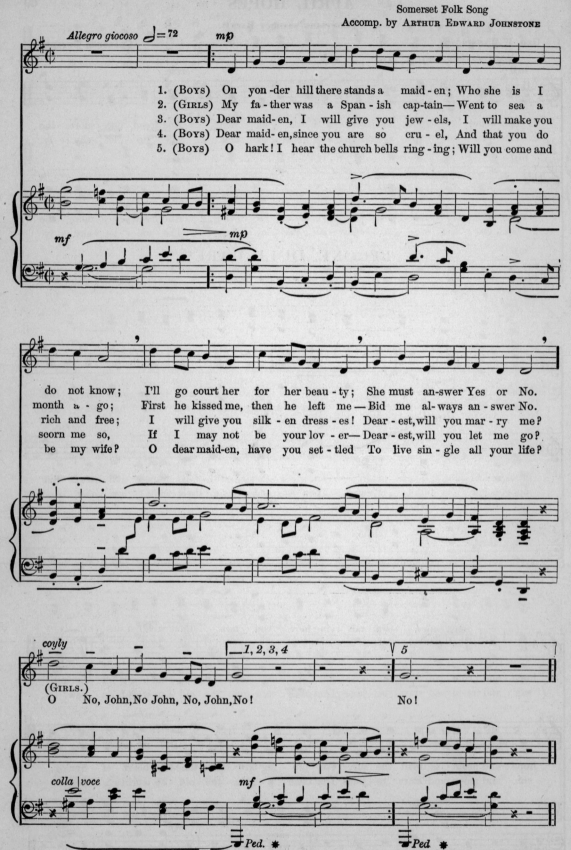

1. (Boys) On yon-der hill there stands a maid-en; Who she is I
2. (Girls) My fa-ther was a Span-ish cap-tain— Went to sea a
3. (Boys) Dear maid-en, I will give you jew-els, I will make you
4. (Boys) Dear maid-en, since you are so cru-el, And that you do
5. (Boys) O hark! I hear the church bells ring-ing; Will you come and

do not know; I'll go court her for her beau-ty; She must an-swer Yes or No.
month a-go; First he kissed me, then he left me—Bid me al-ways an-swer No.
rich and free; I will give you silk-en dress-es! Dear-est, will you mar-ry me?
scorn me so, If I may not be your lov-er— Dear-est, will you let me go?
be my wife? O dear maid-en, have you set-tled To live sin-gle all your life?

coyly

1, 2, 3, 4

5

(Girls.)
O No, John, No John, No, John, No!   No!

colla voce

mf

Ped.   Ped.

APRIL HOPES

(Complete without Bass)

Geo. W. Pennington

Clarence Butler

Moderato (beat two) ♩. = 60

1. The hours of snow and frost have tak - en wing, And freed once more, the
2. The cro - cus cups are decked with gems of dew; The vio - let shy - ly

1. The hours of snow and frost have tak - en wing, And freed once more, the
2. The cro - cus cups are decked with gems of dew; The vio - let shy - ly

brook - lets laugh and sing; The or - chard still is brown and bare, But
opes her eye of blue; The wak - ing for - est lifts her voice, And

brook - lets laugh and sing; The or - chard still is brown and bare, But
opes her eye of blue; The wak - ing for - est lifts her voice, And

Fair hope,
Re - joice,

hope and prom - ise thrill the air, For pip - ing birds have tuned the heart of Spring.
sun and moon and stars re - joice That once a - gain the old - en world is new. .

hope and prom - ise thrill the air, For pip - ing birds have tuned the heart of Spring.
sun and moon and stars re - joice That once a - gain the old - en world is new. .

sweet joy!   The heart of   Spring.
re - joice!   The world is   new. .

LULLABY

(COMPLETE WITHOUT BASS)

C. BELLAMY
SOLO OR UNISON

From " Erminie "
EDWARD JAKOBOWSKI
Four-part arr.

1. Dear moth-er, in dreams I see her . . With face so sweet and calm, . And hear her voice With love re-joice, When nest-ling on her arm . . . I think how she soft-ly press'd me, And tears would dim her eye, . . As in ac-cent mild She sang her child This gen-tle lull-a-

2. And e'en when her life was ebb-ing, . . Her words were all of me; . My fu-ture years Were all her fears; My fate she ne'er could see . . . My fa-ther, I heard him weep-ing, In sad-ness stand-ing nigh, . . As he seemed to hear, In ech-o clear, This ten-der lull-a-

Bye bye! With drow-si-ness o'er-tak - en, Pret - ty lit - tle eye - lids sleep ;   Bye   bye! I

Bye bye,   bye   bye,   bye   bye,   bye bye, Bye bye,

Bye,   bye, ...   bye,   bye,   Bye,

Bye bye,   bye   bye,   bye .   bye,   bye bye, Bye bye,

Ped.   Ped.   * Ped.

watch un - til thou wak - en ; Dar- ling, be thy slum - ber deep. Bye bye, bye bye!

bye   bye,   bye   bye,   dear.

bye,   bye,   bye, Bye bye, bye bye!

bye   bye,   bye   bye,   bye, Bye bye, bye bye!

* Ped.   * Ped.   *

SONG OF A THOUSAND YEARS

(Complete without Bass)

Henry Clay Work

Henry Clay Work
Four-part arr.

Solo or Unison *Vigoroso* ♩=76

1. Lift up your eyes, de-spond-ing foe-men! Fling to the winds your need-less
2. What if the clouds, one lit-tle mo-ment, Hide the blue sky where morn ap-
3. Tell the great world these bless-ed ti-dings! Yes, and be sure the bond-man

fears! He who un-furl'd your beau-teous ban-ner, Says it shall wave a thou-sand years!
pears, When the bright sun that tints them crim-son, Ris-es to shine a thou-sand years!
hears! Tell the op-pressed of ev-'ry na-tion, Ju-bi-lee lasts a thou-sand years!

CHORUS

A thou-sand years! My own Co-lum-bia! 'Tis the glad day so long fore-told.

(Optional Alto)

A thou-sand years! My own Co-lum-bia! 'Tis the glad day so long fore-told.

'Tis the glad morn whose ear-ly twi-light Wash-ing-ton saw in times of old.

'Tis the glad morn whose ear-ly twi-light Wash-ing-ton saw in times of old.

SUNNY SPAIN

(COMPLETE WITHOUT BASS)

FOSTER B. MERRIAM

ARTHUR EDWARD JOHNSTONE

1. A-far, in Spain, O! .. A-cross the main, O! ..
2. From loft-y tow'rs, O! .. Are chimed the hours, O! ..

..There are won-der-ful tow-er-ing moun-tains ris-ing a-bove the
..And the mag-i-cal mu-sic is waft-ed o-ver the gar-den

plain. . . . . . And in that land, O! . . . On ev-'ry
bow'rs. . . . . . In plum-age gay, O! . . . At break of

hand, O! .. Sum-mer flow-ers are blos-som-ing fair, Per-fum-ing the air. O
day, O! .. All the birds are a-wake with a trill, On val-ley and hill. O

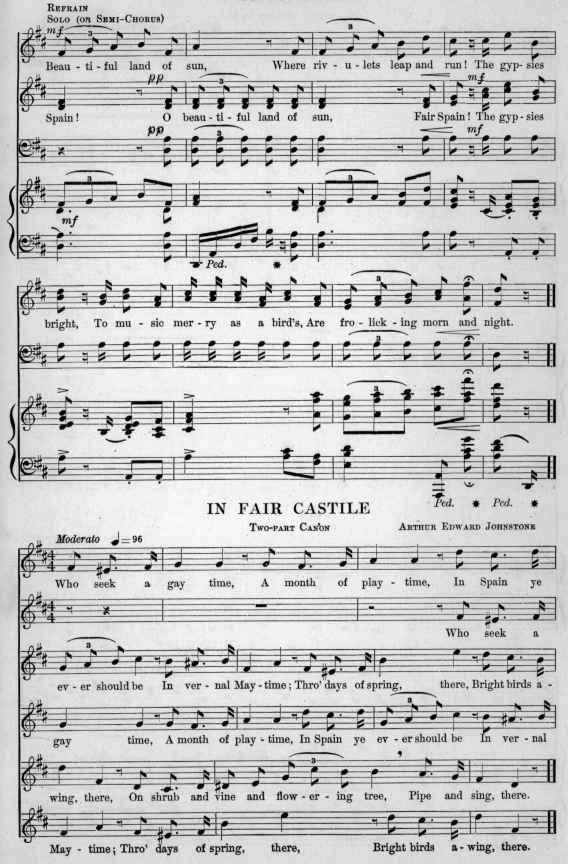

IN FAIR CASTILE

Two-part Canon

Arthur Edward Johnstone

Moderato ♩ = 96

Who seek a gay time, A month of play - time, In Spain ye

Who seek a

ev - er should be In ver - nal May - time; Thro' days of spring, there, Bright birds a -

gay time, A month of play - time, In Spain ye ev - er should be In ver - nal

wing, there, On shrub and vine and flow - er - ing tree, Pipe and sing, there.

May - time; Thro' days of spring, there, Bright birds a - wing, there.

LOCH LOMOND

Scotch Folk Song
Accomp. by CLARENCE BUTLER

1. By yon bon-nie banks and by yon bon-nie braes, Where the sun shines bright on Loch
2. 'Twas then that we part-ed in yon shad-y glen, On the steep, steep side o' Ben
3. The wee bird-ies sing and the wild flow-ers spring, And in sun-shine the wa-ters are

Lo - mond, Where me and my true love were ev-er wont to gae, On the
Lo - mond, Where in pur - ple hue the Hie-land hills we view, And the
sleep - in', But the bro-ken heart may ken nae sec-ond spring a-gain, Tho' the

bon - nie, bon - nie banks o' Loch Lo - mond,
moon looks out in the gloam - in'. } Oh, ye'll tak' the high road and
wae - fu' may cease frae their greet - in'.

I'll tak' the low road, An' I'll be in Scot-land a-fore ye; But me an' my true love will

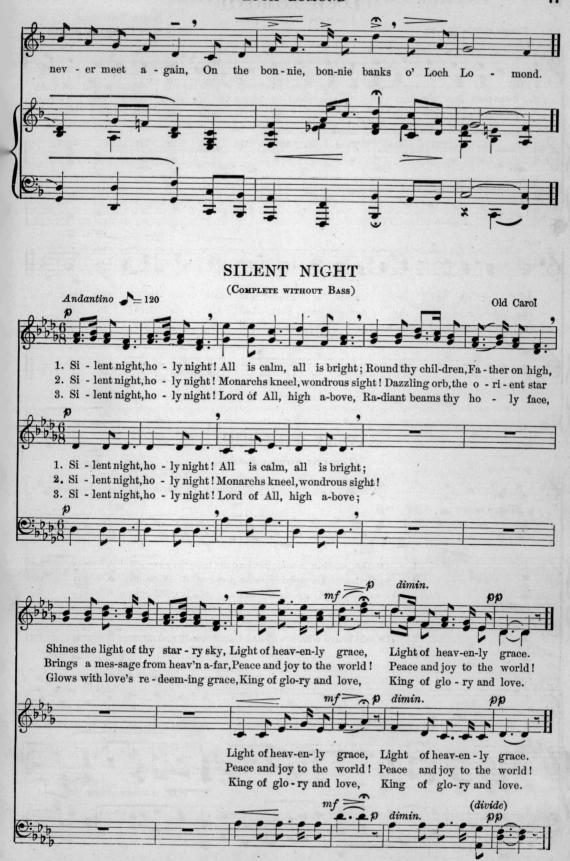

nev - er meet a - gain, On the bon - nie, bon - nie banks o' Loch Lo - mond.

SILENT NIGHT

(Complete without Bass)

Old Carol

Andantino ♩ = 120

1. Si - lent night, ho - ly night! All is calm, all is bright; Round thy chil-dren, Fa - ther on high,
2. Si - lent night, ho - ly night! Monarchs kneel, wondrous sight! Dazzling orb, the o - ri - ent star
3. Si - lent night, ho - ly night! Lord of All, high a-bove, Ra-diant beams thy ho - ly face,

1. Si - lent night, ho - ly night! All is calm, all is bright;
2. Si - lent night, ho - ly night! Monarchs kneel, wondrous sight!
3. Si - lent night, ho - ly night! Lord of All, high a-bove;

Shines the light of thy star - ry sky, Light of heav-en-ly grace, Light of heav-en-ly grace.
Brings a mes-sage from heav'n a-far, Peace and joy to the world! Peace and joy to the world!
Glows with love's re - deem-ing grace, King of glo-ry and love, King of glo - ry and love.

Light of heav-en-ly grace, Light of heav-en - ly grace.
Peace and joy to the world! Peace and joy to the world!
King of glo - ry and love, King of glo - ry and love.

FATHER, WHATE'ER OF EARTHLY BLISS

(Complete without Bass)

H. G. Nägeli

Tranquillo ♩ = 60

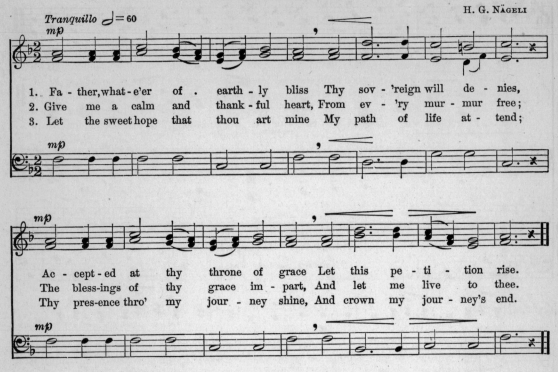

1. Fa - ther, what - e'er of earth - ly bliss Thy sov - 'reign will de - nies,
2. Give me a calm and thank - ful heart, From ev - 'ry mur - mur free;
3. Let the sweet hope that thou art mine My path of life at - tend;

Ac - cept - ed at thy throne of grace Let this pe - ti - tion rise.
The bless-ings of thy grace im - part, And let me live to thee.
Thy pres-ence thro' my jour - ney shine, And crown my jour - ney's end.

AWAY FOR RIO!

(Complete without Bass)

Old Sailor Chantey
Accomp. by Arthur Edward Johnstone

Allegro vivace ♩ = 88 *mp*

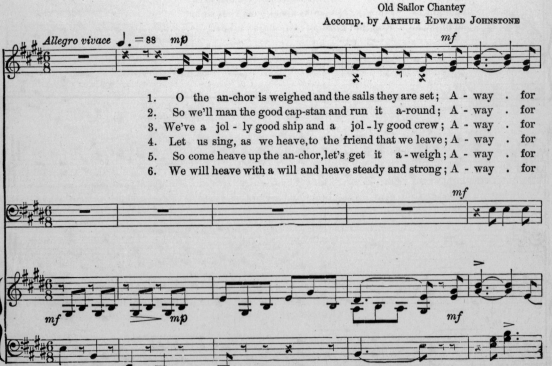

1. O the an-chor is weighed and the sails they are set; A - way . for
2. So we'll man the good cap-stan and run it a-round; A - way . for
3. We've a jol - ly good ship and a jol - ly good crew; A - way . for
4. Let us sing, as we heave, to the friend that we leave; A - way . for
5. So come heave up the an-chor, let's get it a-weigh; A - way . for
6. We will heave with a will and heave steady and strong; A - way . for

Ri - o! The town that we're leav-ing we'll nev - er for-get, For we're bound for Ri - o
Ri - o! We'll heave up the an-chor to this jol-ly sound, For we're bound for Ri - o
Ri - o! A jol-ly good mate and a good skip-per, too, For we're bound for Ri - o
Ri - o! They know at this part-ing how sad-ly we grieve, For we're bound for Ri - o
Ri - o! It's got a firm grip, so heave stead-y, I say, For we're bound for Ri - o
Ri - o! Come, sing a good cho-rus, for 'tis a good song, For we're bound for Ri - o

So a-way! . . . Aye! . . .

Grande. A-way to Ri-o! And aye for Ri-o! Sing

- fare ye well for man-y a day; We are bound for Ri-o Grande!

LET MUSIC WAKE

Russell M. Dodge

J. W. Elliott

Allegro moderato ♩ = 116

1. Let mu - sic wake in joy - ful wise, As - pir - ing to the vault - ed skies, As
2. Let all ex - alt the King a - bove And kin - dle fires of ho - ly love; Thro'

new - ly born The gold - en morn In - vites to high en - deav - or. The Lord is on his
end - less days May psalms of praise Their pow'r re - lin - quish nev - er. E - ter - nal in the

throne, 'Tis he who reigns a - lone. Let all who live re - joice, U -
sky There smiles a watch - ful eye; No mor - tal heart shall fear, Our

nit - ing heart and voice To mag - ni - fy his ho - ly Name for - ev - er!
Fa - ther - Lord is near; Al - might - y One, our souls are thine for - ev - er!

(COMPLETE WITHOUT BASS)

From the Welsh by
ALFRED PERCIVAL GRAVES

JAMES JAMES
Four-part arr.

Vigoroso ♩ = 120

1. O land of my fa-thers, O land of my love, Dear moth-er of min-strels who kin-dle and
2. O land of the mountains, the bird's par-a - dise, Whose prec-i-pice proud, val-leys lone as the
3. For tho' the fierce foe-man has rav-aged your realm, The old speech of Cym-ru he can-not o'er-

move, And he - ro on he - ro, who at honor's proud call, For free-dom their life-blood let fall. .
skies, Green murmuring for-est, far - ech-o - ing flood Fire the fan-cy and quick-en the blood. .
whelm, Our pas-sion-ate po - ets to . si-lence com-mand Or . ban-ish the harp from your strand.

Wales! . Wales! . Oh, but my heart is with you! . . And

long as the sea Your bul-wark shall be, To Cym-ru my heart shall be true. . .

INDIAN SUMMER

(COMPLETE WITHOUT BASS)

JOHN GREENLEAF WHITTIER

E. W. JOHNS

Andante ♩ = 69

1. From gold to gray One wild, sweet day Of In-dian sum-mer fades too soon; . But
(2ND SOP.) fades ... too soon;
2. In its pale fire The vil-lage spire Shows like the zo-diac's spec-tral lance; . The
(2ND SOP.) spec - - tral lance;

1. From gold to gray One wild, sweet day Of In-dian sum-mer fades too soon; . . But
2. In its pale fire The vil-lage spire Shows like the zo-diac's spec-tral lance; . . The

But ten -
The paint-

(For rehearsal only)

p legato

rall.

ten - der - ly A - bove the sea . . Hangs, white and calm, the hun - ter's moon.
paint - ed walls Where - on it falls . Trans-fig - ured stand in mar - ble trance.

rall.

ten - der - ly A - bove the sea . Hangs, white and calm, the hun - ter's moon.
paint - ed walls Where - on it falls . Trans-fig - ured stand in mar - ble trance.

rall. (divide ad lib.)

- - der - ly A - bove . .
- - ed walls Where - on . .

rall.

ALMA MATER

Harvey Worthington Loomis

Arthur Edward Johnstone

1. Our thoughts are held in lov - ing thrall To fair Mi - ner - va's hon - ored Hall
2. Loved Al - ma Ma - ter's peace - ful bow'rs Are wreathed with Art's e - ter - nal flow'rs;
3. The sa - ge's scroll, the min - strel's lay, 'Tis here we've conned from day to day;

Whose i - vied tow'rs of slen - der grace Have made for doves a dwell - ing - place;
Grave Learn - ing's paths, from June to June With La - bor's fruits are rich - ly strewn.
With - in these walls we've pon - dered o'er The price - less pearls of gar - nered lore.

Whose bells of sil - ver thrill the air And set the hours to mu - sic rare,
While sea - sons change from green to white And day gives place to star - lit night,
But best of Wis-dom's guer - dons fair, The prize of all be - yond com - pare,

A song that e'er, as years de-part, Shall chime a - gain in each fond heart.
The Flame of Faith, the Torch of Truth, Shall ev - er guide the steps of Youth.
Our loy - al friend-ship's flow'r di - vine That bides in Mem - 'ry's fra-grant shrine.

THE MEETING OF THE WATERS

Thomas Moore

Irish Folk Tune
Accomp. by M. W. Balfe

Allegretto espressivo ♪ = 112

1. There is not in the wide world a val - ley so sweet
2. Yet it was not that Na - ture had shed o'er the scene
3. 'Twas that friends, the be - lov'd of my bos - om, were near,
4. Sweet vale of A - vo - ca! how calm could I rest

As that
Her
Who made
In thy

vale in whose bos - om the bright wa - ters meet;* Oh, the last rays of
pur - est of crys - tal and bright-est of green; 'Twas not her soft
ev - 'ry dear scene of en - chant-ment more dear; And who felt how the
bos - om of shade, with the friends I love best; Where the storms that we

feel - ing and life must de - part, Ere the bloom of that val - ley shall
mag - ic of stream - let or rill, Oh, . no — it was some - thing more
best charms of Na - ture im - prove, When we see them re - flect - ed from
feel in this cold world should cease, And our hearts, like thy wa - ters, be

* The rivers Avon and Avoca

rit. *a tempo* *rall.*

fade from my heart, Ere the bloom of that val - ley shall fade from my heart!
ex - qui - site still, Oh, . . no— it was some-thing more ex - qui - site still!
looks that we love, When we see them re - flect - ed from looks that we love.
min - gled in peace, And our hearts, like thy wa - ters, be min - gled in peace!

rit. *a tempo* *p* *rall.*

FIERCE RAGED THE TEMPEST
(Complete without Bass)

GODFREY THRING   JOHN B. DYKES

mf Moderato ♩ = 104

1. Fierce raged the tem - pest o'er the deep, Watch did thine anx - ious
2. "Save, Lord, we per - ish," was their cry, "O save us in our
3. The wild winds hushed; the an - gry deep Sank, like a lit - tle
4. So when our life is cloud - ed o'er, And storm-winds drift us

mf

1. Fierce raged the tem - pest o'er the deep, Watch did thine anx - ious
2. "Save, Lord, we per - ish," was their cry, "O save us in our
3. The wild winds hushed; the an - gry deep Sank, like a lit - tle
4. So when our life is cloud - ed o'er, And storm-winds drift us

mf

mp *p*

ser - vants keep; But thou wast wrapped in guile - less sleep, Calm and still. . .
ag - o - ny!" Thy word a - bove the storm rose high, "Peace, be still!" .
child, to sleep; The sul - len bil - lows ceased to leap At thy will. . .
from the shore, Say, lest we sink to rise no more, "Peace, be still!" .

mp *p*

ser - vants keep; But thou wast wrapped in guile - less sleep, Calm and still. . .
ag - o - ny!" Thy word a - bove the storm rose high, "Peace, be still!" .
child, to sleep; The sul - len bil - lows ceased to leap At thy will. . .
from the shore, Say, lest we sink to rise no more, "Peace, be still!" .

mp *p*

GOD IS OUR REFUGE

(INTEGER VITAE)

(Complete without Bass)

F. F. Flemming

Maestoso ♩ = 108

1. God is our ref - uge, stead - fast and un - shak - en,
2. There - fore we fear not, sure of our sal - va - tion,
3. There is a riv - er, gen - tly on it glid - eth,

1. God is our ref - uge, stead - fast and un - shak - en,
2. There - fore we fear not, sure of our sal - va - tion,
3. There is a riv - er, gen - tly on it glid - eth,

Shield - ing us safe - ly when the storms a - wak - en; Ne'er shall his
E'en though the moun - tains shake to their foun - da - tion; Though earth be
Wa - t'ring the cit - y where our Lord a - bid - eth; Who to its

Shield - ing us safe - ly when the storms a - wak - en; Ne'er shall his
E'en though the moun - tains shake to their foun - da - tion; Though earth be
Wa - t'ring the cit - y where our Lord a - bid - eth; Who to its

chil - dren be by him for - sak - en; His hand sus - tains . us.
mov - ed, fright - ened ev - 'ry na - tion, God's love is o'er . . us.
heal - ing all his ills con - fid - eth, Nev - er shall per - ish.

chil - dren be by him for - sak - en; His hand sus - tains . us.
mov - ed, fright - ened ev - 'ry na - tion, God's love is o'er . . us.
heal - ing all his ills con - fid - eth, Nev - er shall per - ish.

Words adapted by KATHARINE WHITMORE

Old Sailor Chantey
Accomp. written for this work

1. 'Twas on the gay At-lan-tic   'Mid E-qui-noc-tial gales,   A
2. They sent a boat to find him   And rowed a-round the sea;   They
3. He said, "I've met the fish-es,   And find they swim quite well;   I

sail-or boy went o-ver-board   A-mong the sharks and whales;   He
saw him soon, but all he said   Was "Don't you cry for me!   I
tried to eat a her-mit-crab   But could not break his shell.   And

dis-ap-peared quite quick-ly   With-in the brin-y waves,   Sing-ing,
just have seen a mer-maid   A-mong the o-cean caves,   Sing-ing,
now he's learn-ing mu-sic;   He reads it from the staves,   Sing-ing,

"Brit-ons nev-er, nev-er, nev-er will be slaves!"

O TEMPORA! O MORES!

(COMPLETE WITHOUT BASS)

College Song
Accomp. written for this work

Allegro giocoso ♩ = 100

1. {
There went a fid - dler march - ing, a - march - ing on the Nile,
There crept from out the wa - ter a mon - strous croc - o - dile;
}

2. {
Then up the fid - dler took at once his cun - ning bow with care,
And from his an - cient fid - dle drew such tones of mu - sic rare;
}

O

3. {
And when the fid - dle sound - ed be - neath his skill - ful hands,
The croc - o - dile be - gan to dance up - on the des - ert sands.
}

4. {
And now this song is end - ed the mor - al's near to seek,
It is not well to spend your time a - lone in learn - ing Greek.
}

O

Tem - po - ra! O Mo - res!

{
And as it fain would
Al - le - gro, dol - ce,
Quad - rilles, ga - vottes, and
But learn at once to
}

swal - low him, such teeth you nev - er saw!
pres - to; such tunes you nev - er saw!
waltz - es; such steps you nev - er saw!
fid - dle; such sport you nev - er saw!

Fal - lal - la - la - la - la,

O

Tem - po, tem - po - ra, To thee be praise for end-less days, Dame Mu - si - ca.

NEVERMORE

FOSTER B. MERRIAM

(COMPLETE WITHOUT BASS*)

Folk Tune

Allegro moderato ♩ = 126

1. The clouds re - call their rain - drops nev - er - more; Their fleec - y folds may
2. The van - ished breeze brings per - fume nev - er - more; Its gen - tle voice may
3. Fair yes - ter's morn shall greet us nev - er - more; Its song of joy shall

(BASS MELODY)*

Nev - er - more; The clouds drift
Nev - er - more; It wings thro'
Nev - er - more; The gold must

hold them nev - er - more; And e'en the clouds drift off like a fleet on an
charm us nev - er - more; It wings its way thro' gar - dens a - far till the
wake us nev - er - more; Its hours of gold must fade in the night, tho' their

To re - turn nev - er - more.

o - cean that knows not a shore, To re - turn . nev - er - more.
hours of its mu - sic are o'er, To re - turn . nev - er - more.
pass - ing how - e'er we de - plore, To re - turn . nev - er - more.

* In the absence of basses, this melody may be taken by unchanged voices.

THE SONG AMERICA SINGS

(COMPLETE WITHOUT BASS)

HARVEY WORTHINGTON LOOMIS

ARTHUR EDWARD JOHNSTONE

1. Land of the brave,
2. Land of the brave,

land of the free, land of the true, home of the daunt-less he - ro,
land of the free, land of the true, shrine of the pa - triot's hom - age,

proud do thy ban-ners wave! . . . . From North to the South . . is heard the
hope of the pil-grim's heart! . . . . As breeze to the breeze . . im-parts the

truth . . we fight for last - ing peace,   the road il - lum-ined by the glow of Lib - er - ty's

torch; flame . of ho - li - est light, the sun that nev-er shall set,   the fire . . that was kin-dled on

high   to burn . as a bea-con e - ter - nal . where A - mer - i-ca's flag is fly - ing.

A HUNDRED YEARS AGO

(COMPLETE WITHOUT BASS)

EDWIN STAR BELKNAP

Old Sailor Chantey
Accomp. written for this work

Allegro giocoso ♩ = 88

Yo, heave ho!

1. A hun-dred years is a ver-y long time, Yo, heave ho!
2. I'd like to know if the sto-ry is true: Yo, heave ho!
3. The West was still but a des-o-late plain, Yo, heave ho!
4. The birds that fly to get high-er and high'r, Yo, heave ho!
5. Da-ri-us Green, with his fly-ing ma-chine, Yo, heave ho!
6. They nev-er raced in a gas-o-line fly'r, Yo, heave ho!
7. They chased the hour with their frol-ic and fun, Yo, heave ho!
8. Let those who will for lon-gev-i-ty strive, Yo, heave ho!

And yet, 'tis said they were singing this rime A hun-dred years a-go.
I've heard the sky was a ver-y bright blue A hun-dred years a-go.
For naught they knew of a "lim-it-ed" train A hun-dred years a-go.
Could not have flown to a tel-e-phone wire A hun-dred years a-go.
Would still be here, if he'd been a bit keen A hun-dred years a-go.
They nev-er punc-tured a bi-cy-cle tire A hun-dred years a-go.
But none had yet made a "cen-tu-ry run" A hun-dred years a-go.
But oh, I'm glad that I was-n't a-live A hun-dred years a-(*Omit.* . . .) go.

A hun-dred years a-go. go.

THE MARSEILLAISE

ROUGET DE LISLE
SOLO (OR UNISON)

(COMPLETE WITHOUT BASS)

ROUGET DE LISLE
Accomp. written for this work

1. Ye sons of free - dom, wake to glo - ry! Hark! hark! what myr - iads bid you
2. Now, now the dan-g'rous storm is roll - ing, Which wick - ed men con - fed - 'rate
3. O lib - er - ty! can man re - sign thee, Once hav - ing felt thy gen - 'rous

rise! Your children, wives, and grandsires hoar - y, Be-hold their tears and hear their
raise; The dogs of war let loose are howl - ing, And lo! our walls and cit - ies
flame? Can dun-geons, bolts and bars con - fine thee, Or whips thy no - ble spir - it

cries, Be-hold their tears and hear their cries! Shall hate-ful ty-rants, mis - chief
blaze! And shall we base - ly view the scene, While law-less force with guilt-y
tame, Or whips thy no - ble spir - it . tame? Too long the world has wept, be -

breeding With hire-ling hosts, a ruf - fian band, Af - fright and des - o - late the
stride Spreads des - o - la-tion far and wide, Spreads des - o - la-tion far and
wail-ing That false-hood's dag-ger ty - rants wield, But free - dom is our sword and

land,   While   peace and lib - er - ty   lie bleed - ing?
wide   With   crimes and blood his hands em - bru - ing?
shield,   And   all   their arts are un - a - vail - ing.

REFRAIN

To arms,   to arms, ye brave! Th' a - ven - ging sword un-sheathe! March on, . . march

To arms,   to arms, ye brave! Th' a - ven - ging sword un-sheathe! March on, . . march

March on,

on,   all hearts re - solved . On vic - to - ry or death!

on,   all hearts re - solved . On vic - to - ry or death!

march, on .

THE MINSTREL'S REQUEST

(COMPLETE WITHOUT BASS)

JOHN E. WEST

1. Sum-mer eve is gone and
2. I have sung of war for

past, Sum-mer dew is fall-ing fast; I have wandered all the day, Do not
knight, Lay of love for la - dy bright, Fair-y tale to lull the heir, Gob - lin

bid me 'far - ther stray; Gen - tle hearts of gen - tle kin, . Take the wan - d'ring
grim the maids to scare; Dark the night, and long till day, . Do not bid me

harp   and   for the bard;   Bar-on's face throve nev - er   well . .   Where the

curse of min - strel fell: . .   If   you love your no - ble kin, .

COME BACK TO ERIN

(COMPLETE WITHOUT BASS)

"CLARIBEL"   "CLARIBEL" (MRS. CHARLES BARNARD)

1. Come back to E-rin, Ma-vour-neen, Ma-vour-neen, Come back, A-roon, to the
2. O-ver the green sea, Ma-vour-neen, Ma-vour-neen, Long shone the white sail that
3. Oh, may the an-gels o' wak-in' and sleep-in', Watch o'er my bird in the

land of thy birth; Come with the sham-rocks and spring-time, Ma-vour-neen,
bore thee a-way; Rid-ing the white waves that fair sum-mer morn-in'
land far a-way; And it's my pray'rs will con-sign to their keep-in'

And it's Kil-lar-ney shall ring with our mirth. Sure when we lent ye to
Just like a May-flow'r a-float on the bay. Oh, but my heart sank when
Care of my jew-el by night and by day. When by the fire-side I

beau-ti-ful Eng-land, Lit-tle we thought of the lone win-ter days,
clouds came be-tween us! Like a grey cur-tain, the rain fall-ing down,
watch the bright em-bers, Then all my heart flies to Eng-land and thee,

Lit - tle we thought of the hush of the star - shine O - ver the moun - tain, the
Hid from my sad eyes the path o'er the o - cean Far, far a - way where my
Crav - in' to know if my dar - lin' re - mem - bers, Or if her thoughts may be

Chorus *Tempo primo*

bluffs and the braes! Then, come back to E - rin, Ma - vour - neen, Ma - vour - neen;
Col - leen had flown.
cross - in' to me.

Tempo primo

Come back a - gain to the land of thy birth. Come back to E - rin, Ma-
Ah,

allargando
cresc.

vour - neen, Ma - vour - neen, And its Kil - lar - ney shall ring with our mirth.
cresc.

allargando

cresc.

SANTA LUCIA *

(COMPLETE WITHOUT BASS)

Neapolitan Folk Tune
Accomp. written for this work

A district of Naples named after its patron saint.

Home of fair Po - e - sy, Realm of pure Har - mo - ny, San - ta Lu - ci - a, San - ta Lu - ci - a!

SWING LOW, SWEET CHARIOT

(COMPLETE WITHOUT BASS)

"Spiritual"

Rubato
SOLO (OR UNISON)   *p* CHORUS

Swing low, sweet char - i - ot, . Com - in' fo' to car - ry me home,

SOLO   CHORUS   *pp* FINE

Swing low, sweet char - i - ot, . Com - in' fo' to car - ry me home.

mf SOLO   *mf* CHORUS

1. I looked o - ver Jor - dan and what did I see,
2. If you get there be - fore I do,
3. The bright - est day that ev - er I saw,
4. I'm some - times up and some - times down,
} Com - in' fo' to car - ry me home,

SOLO   *mf* CHORUS   *p* D.C.

A band of an - gels com - in' aft - er me,
Tell all my friends I'm com - in' too,
When Je - sus washed my sins a - way,
But still my soul feels heav'n - ly bound,
} Com - in' fo' to car - ry me home.

FATHER, TEACH ME

(COMPLETE WITHOUT BASS)

JANE E. LEESON

CARL MARIA VON WEBER

1. Fa - ther, teach me, day by .. day, Love's sweet les - son to o - bey;
2. Teach me all thy steps to .. trace, Strong to fol - low in thy grace,
3. Love in lov - ing finds em - ploy, In o - be - dience all her joy;

Sweet - er les - son can - not be, Lov - ing him who first loved me.
Learn - ing how to love from thee, Lov - ing him who first loved me.
Ev - er new that joy will be, Lov - ing him who first loved me.

POLISH NATIONAL SONG

(COMPLETE WITHOUT BASS)

From the Polish
by FREDERICK WINTHROP

Melody by SOWINSKI
Accomp. written for this work

1. Sons of Po - land, strive a - gain, Tho' the a - lien horde sur-round you;
2. Law - less hosts de - fy the Lord In a lust that maims and slaugh-ters;
3. Hark, the con - queror sing - ing clear, With the dawn of Peace be - fore us;

Be the same staunch, loy-al men That the days of yore have found you!
Rise, a-venge with na-ked sword Bleed-ing Po-land's wives and daugh-ters!
See the vi-sion bright ap-pear, 'Tis the flag of Free-dom o'er us!

Free-dom calls a-cross the sea, Lights a-gain her ho-ly torch for thee; Once the shackles but to

sev-er, Po-land's free for-ev-er! Po-land's free for-ev-er!

HEAVENLY CONCORD
(COMPLETE WITHOUT BASS)

FELIX KEUNDIG

Tranquillo ♩ = 108

1. Heav - en - ly con - cord, im - age of love, Send us thy pres - ence
2. O thou up - lift - est grand - ly the soul, Giv - ing us cour - age
3. Lord, if e'er dis - cord ris - es to - day, May it be quick - ly

down from a - bove; Let thy light en - ter each lov - ing heart, . . Heav - en - ly
un - to the goal; Com - fort - ing ev - er trou - ble and pain, . . That in the
driv - en a - way; Help us to meet it with a bright smile, . . Give us sweet

con - cord, nev - er de - part; Heav - en - ly con - cord, nev - er de - part.
spir - it, glad - ness may reign; That in the spir - it, . glad - ness may reign.
con - cord, ban - ish - ing guile; Give us sweet con - cord, ban - ish - ing guile.

Two-Part Canon

Thomas Tallis
16th Century

Moderato ♩ = 69

1. Ac - cept our praise, O God, this night For all the bless - ings
bless - ings flow: Praise him, all crea - tures

(2d stanza f)

1. Ac - cept our praise, O God, this night For
God from whom all bless - ings flow: Praise

of the light; Keep me, O keep me, King of Kings, Be - neath thy own Al -
here be - low! Praise him, ye heav'n - ly host a - bove! Praise him, my soul, for

all the bless - ings of the light: Keep me, O keep me, King of Kings, Be -
him, all crea - tures here be - low! Praise him, ye heav'n - ly host a - bove! Praise

might-y wings. 2. Praise God, from whom all all his love! A - MEN.

neath thy own Al - might - y wings. 2. Praise him, my soul, for all his love! A - MEN.

A WARRIOR BOLD

(Complete without Bass)

Edwin Thomas

Stephen Adams
Three-part arr.

1. In days of old, when knights were bold And bar-ons held their sway, A war-rior bold, with spurs of gold, Sang mer-ri-ly his lay, . . . Sang mer-ri-ly his lay: "My love is young and fair, My love hath gold-en hair, And eyes so blue, and heart so true, That

2. So this brave knight, in ar-mor bright, Went gay-ly to the fray; He fought the fight, but ere the night, His soul had pass'd a-way, . . . His soul had pass'd a-way. The plight-ed ring he wore Was crushed and wet with gore, Yet ere he died, he brave-ly cried, "I've

none with her com-pare, So what care I, tho' death be nigh? I'll live for love or
kept the vow I swore. So what care I, tho' death be nigh? I've fought for love and

allargando

die, So what care I, tho' death be nigh? I'll live for love or die."

THE LORD'S PRAYER

(COMPLETE WITHOUT BASS)

ARTHUR EDWARD JOHNSTONE

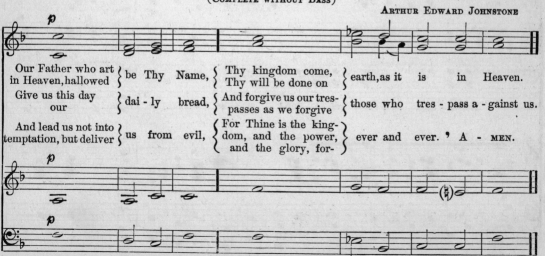

Our Father who art in Heaven, hallowed { be Thy Name, { Thy kingdom come, Thy will be done on { earth, as it is in Heaven.

Give us this day our { dai-ly bread, { And forgive us our tres-passes as we forgive { those who tres-pass a-gainst us.

And lead us not into temptation, but deliver { us from evil, { For Thine is the king-dom, and the power, and the glory, for- { ever and ever. ' A-MEN.

ON PARADE

(COMPLETE WITHOUT BASS)

KATHARINE WHITMORE

HARVEY WORTHINGTON LOOMIS

Allegro marziale ♩. = 92

Thou-sands of sol - diers on the march pass in gal-lant ar - ray. . . .

They're on the march in gal-lant ar - ray, in gal-lant ar - ray. Oh, hear the

Thou-sands of brave men march, march by, this day. . . .

mf (Optional accompaniment)

Trump - ets blend . . . with fifes . . . . in meas - ure gay. O - ver the

drums . . . and the shrill call of the bu - gle mu - sic loud and gay!

Rub - a - dub, . . . rub - a - dub! Boom, boom, boom! . .

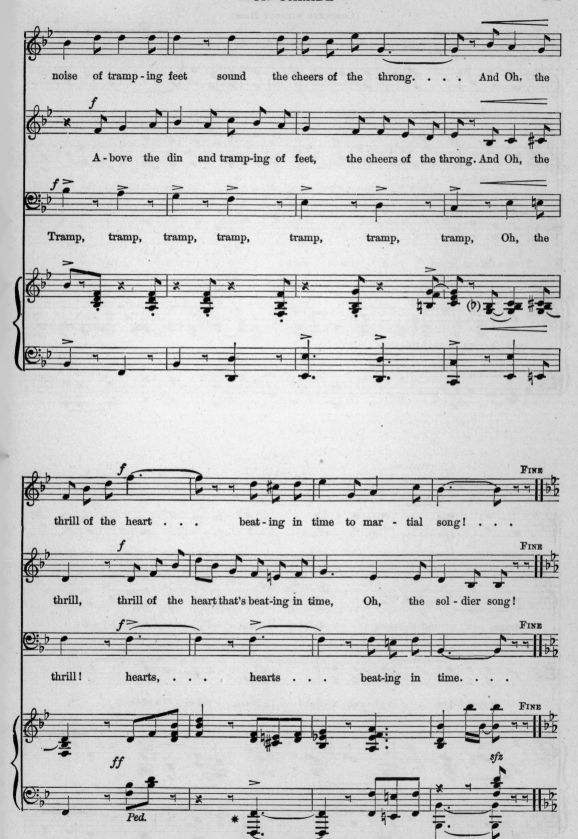

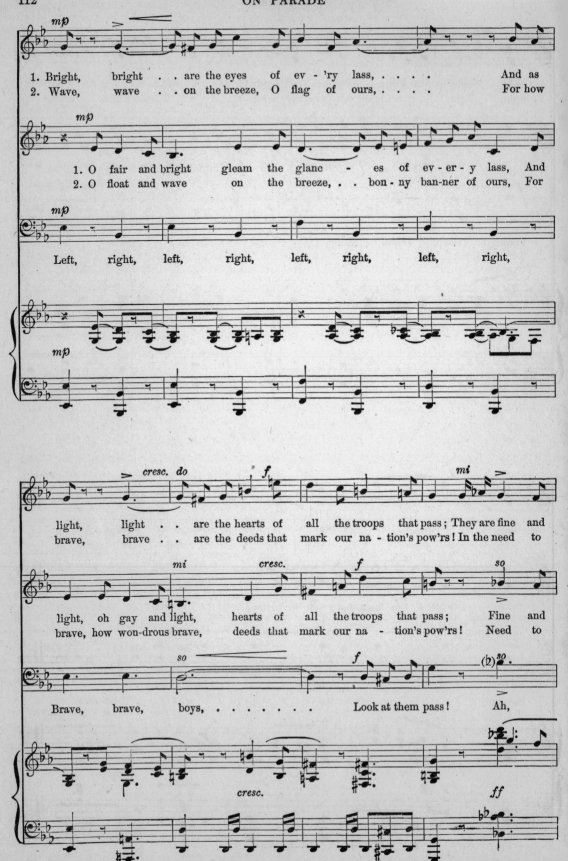

1. Bright,   bright   . . are the eyes   of ev - 'ry lass, ...   And as
2. Wave,   wave   . . on the breeze, O flag of ours, ...   For how

1. O fair and bright   gleam   the   glanc - es   of ev - er - y   lass,   And
2. O float and wave   on   the   breeze, . . bon - ny ban-ner of ours,   For

Left,   right,   left,   right,   left,   right,   left,   right,

light,   light   . . are the hearts of   all   the troops   that pass ; They are fine   and
brave,   brave   . . are the deeds that   mark our na - tion's pow'rs ! In the need   to

light, oh gay and light,   hearts of   all   the troops   that pass ;   Fine   and
brave, how won-drous brave,   deeds that mark our na - tion's pow'rs !   Need   to

Brave,   brave,   boys, ...   Look at them pass !   Ah,

bold, bold . . and their step is firm and true. . . . While the gold, gold
fight, fight . . to maintain a wor-thy peace . . . Till the Right, Right

bold, O ev - er bold step - ping out . . in their u - ni-form trim ; The brighest of gold
fight ? Then must we fight, all for peace . and in lib - er-ty's name. Till Might had the right

Left, right, left, right, left, right, left, right, left. See-ing it

sun crowns their flag with glo - ry new. Thou-sands of
won, not a man of us would cease. Thou-sands of

crown - ing their proud flag with glo - ry new.
con - quer - ors, no man of us would cease.

through, o - ver the top they'll go ! Thou-sands of

CHARLIE IS MY DARLING

(JACOBITE SONG)

(COMPLETE WITHOUT BASS)

Lady Nairne

Scotch Tune
Arr. by John E. West

1. 'Twas on a Mon-day morn-ing, Right ear-ly in the year, When
2. As he cam' march-in' up the street, The pipes play'd loud and clear, And
3. Wi' Hie-land bon-nets on their heads, And Clay-mores bright and clear, They
4. They've left their bon-nie Hie-land hills, Their wives and bairn-ies dear, To

Char - lie came to our . . town, The . . young Chev - a - lier.
a' the folk cam' rin - nin' out To . . meet the Chev - a - lier.
cam' to fight for Scot - land's right And the young Chev - a - lier.
draw the sword for Scot - land's lord, The . . young Chev - a - lier.

BONNIE CHARLIE

(JACOBITE SONG)

(COMPLETE WITHOUT BASS)

Lady NAIRNE

Scotch Folk Song
Three-part arr.

Allegretto espressivo   ♩ = 66

OPTIONAL ALTO SOLO (OR UNISON)

1. Bon - nie Char - lie's noo a - wa', Safe - ly owre the friend - ly main; Mon - y a heart will
3. Hills he trod were all his ain, Bed be - neath the birk - en tree; The bush that hid him
3. Sweet the lav - 'rock's note and lang, Lilt - in' wild - ly up the glen, But aye to me he
4. Mon - y a gal - lant sod - ger fought, Mon - y a gal - lant chief did fa'; Death it - self were

BASS SOLO (OR UNISON)

break in twa Should he ne'er come back a - gain.
on the plain, None on earth can claim but he.
sings ae sang: "Will ye no come back a - gain?"
dear - ly bought A' for Scot - land's King and law.

} Will ye no come back a - gain?

Will ye no come back a - gain? Bet - ter lo'ed ye can - na' be, Will ye no come back a - gain?

THE THREE KINGS

Provençal Air
Accomp. by Gabriel Pierné

Late one night I met up-on my way The three wise Kings of the O-rient

rid - ing; One bright star was guid-ing by its ray The pil-grims three o'er the des-ert sand.

And in their train, load-ed down with gold, There fol-lowed slaves and war-riors

bold; The treas-ure rare, such a price-less store, With shield and spear they were guarding o'er.

THE EVERGREEN

(COMPLETE WITHOUT BASS)

Tune "My Maryland"
Arr. for this work

1. O ev - er - green, fair ev - er - green, Thy pur - ple shad - ow cast - ing!
2. O ev - er - green, fair ev - er - green, With fes - tive can - dles glow - ing!

'Neath sum - mer sun or win - ter sky Thy ver - dant boughs de - light the eye!
Thy mag - ic fruit at Christ - mas eve, Both rich and poor a - like re - ceive.

'Neath sum - mer sun or win - ter sky Thy ver - dant boughs de - light the eye!
Thy mag - ic fruit at Christ - mas eve, Both rich and poor a - like re - ceive.

O ev - er - green, fair ev - er - green, Of beau - ty ev - er - last - ing!
O ev - er - green, fair ev - er - green, Thy boun - ty free be - stow - ing!

O ev - er - green, fair ev - er - green, Of beau - ty ev - er - last - ing!
O ev - er - green, fair ev - er - green, Thy boun - ty free be - stow - ing!

*In the absence of basses, these four measures may be sung by unchanged voices.

BEYOND THE HORIZON

(COMPLETE WITHOUT BASS)

Harvey Worthington Loomis

John Henry Cornell

1. There's a won - der - ful land at the edge of the world, Where the
2. 'Tis a land where the rain - bow's e - van - ish - ing hue Is dis -
3. And should ev - er a mor - tal make quest of that goal, Tho' he

sky and the far - a - way meet; 'Tis a mag - ic - al gar - den with
solved in mys - te - ri - ous light; Like a love - ly mi - rage it will
jour - neyed in Peg - a - sus' car; Ev - er back - ward in dis - tance, like

dew - drops em - pearled, Set to mu - sic en - tranc - ing - ly sweet.
melt from the view As the stars that burn out with the night.
time 'twould un - roll, While its glo - ries still beck - oned a - far.

PART THREE

SOPRANO, SECOND SOPRANO, ALTO, (OR ALTO-TENOR) AND BASS

A TWILIGHT SONG

H. W. L.

HARVEY WORTHINGTON LOOMIS

Good-night! . . . Fades the

1. Out of the west the sun is sink - ing, O - ver the far ho - ri - zon's
2. Trem - u - lous pur - ple heav'n-ward steal - ing, Quench-ing the em - bers in the
3. Van-ished the day, its joy and sor - row; Back in - to heav - en tak - ing

light, the light. . .

Ten - der - ly day and twi - light
Glim - mer of eve - ning star re -
Leav - ing fair prom - ise of the

rim, ...
clouds, ...
flight, ...

Fair day, ... good -

link - ing,
veal - ing,
mor - row,

Smil - ing ere az - ure skies grow dim. . .
Soft - ly the west - 'ring sky en - shrouds. .
Bid - ding a wea - ry world good - night. . .

night! . . .

Smil - ing ere az - ure skies grow dim. . .
Soft - ly the west - 'ring sky en - shrouds. .
Bid - ding a wea - ry world good - night. . .

(divide)

119

THE CALL OF THE SPRING

(COMPLETE WITHOUT BASS)

Alfred Noyes†

John E. West

* In the absence of basses, these four measures may be sung by unchanged voices.
† Words copyright, 1913, by Frederick A. Stokes Company.

THE STORM KING

MARGARET McELROY

JOHN E. WEST

whis - tles and howls . . a bat - tle song . . The while a spell o'er the
teach me to sing . . the bat - tle song . . That chills the heart of the
on - ly the storm . . has pow'r to send . . This wind - born call through the

whis - tles and howls a bat - tle song . . The while a spell o'er the
teach me to sing the bat - tle song . . That chills the heart of the
on - ly the storm has pow'r to send . . This wind - born call through the

world he binds: . "Too - whoo! Too - whoo!
world to - night. . "Too - whoo! Too - whoo!
mist and night. . "Too - whoo! Too - whoo!

world he binds; . "Too - whoo! Too - whoo!
world to - night. . "Too - whoo! Too - whoo!
mist and night. . "Too - whoo! Too - whoo!

"Too - whoo! . . . . . . Too - whoo! . . . . . Too -

Ped. mf

Too-whoo, . too-whoo! Too-whoo, too-whoo! Too-whoo, too-whoo!

Too-whoo, . too-whoo! Too-whoo, too-whoo! Too-whoo, too-whoo!

whoo, . . too-whoo! . At the crack of my whip . The for - est oaks bend left and

With Ped.

Too-whoo, too-whoo! Too-whoo! Too-whoo! Too-whoo! Too-whoo!

Too-whoo, too-whoo! Too-whoo! Too-whoo! Too-whoo! Too-whoo!

right; . . . . Let no man dare . . to cross my path, For

marcato *f* *riten.*

For I, the Storm, am King to - night." ....

marcato *f* *riten.*

For I, the Storm, am King to - night." ....

riten.

I, ... the Storm, ... am King ... to - night." ....

f marcato *riten.*

Ped. ✳

THE POOR OLD MAN

Old Sailor Chantey
Four-part arr.

Lively ♩=96

mp (SOLO VOICES) *, p*

1. O a poor old man came a - rid - ing by, Says I, "Old man, your horse will die!" O
2. O the poor old man, not a word says he, But chains his horse up to a tree. O
3. Mer - ry mess-mates all, if ye like this song, Just keep a - sing - ing all night long. O

mp (SOLO VOICES) *, p*

(*All stanzas*) Yo ho! ......

CHORUS *f*

John-ny, come to Hi - lo, O poor old man! O wake her, O shake her, O

O wake her, O shake her,

(BASS MELODY) CHORUS *f*

, p *,mf*

shake that girl with the blue dress on, O John-ny, come to Hi - lo, O poor old man!

That girl with the

, p *,f*

THE MARINERS

Alfred Noyes*

E. W. Johns

Allegro con brio ♩. = 84

f

Ped.　✳　Ped.　✳　Ped.　✳　Ped.　✳

Solo (or Unison)

mf

mf

Ped.　✳

1. Good luck be - fall you mar - i - ners all That sail this world so
2. And now they plough to wind - ward, now They drive be - fore the

wide! . . Whith - er we go, not yet we know; We steer by wind and
gale! . . Now they are hurl'd a - cross the world With torn and tat - ter'd

p　*poco cresc.*

p　*poco cresc.*

tide; . . Be it right or wrong, I sing this song, For now it seems to
sail; . . Yet, as they will, they steer and still De - fy the world's rude

*The accompaniment is essential throughout.

croon.

Take their si-lent way. Now the fair eve-ning star Sheds her sil-ver light,
Wea-ry earth's at rest. Hon-ey-sweet, rich as gold, Comes a folk re-frain,

ALTO

Take their si-lent way. Croon, Croon,
Wea-ry earth's at rest. Croon, Croon,

sempre legato

Woos the soul of night, woos the soul of night, woos the soul of night.
Ech - o o'er a-gain, ech-o o'er a-gain, ech-o o'er a-gain!

Clear and pure shines a-far, Woos the night, woos the night, woos the night.
Well - be-loved ca-dence old, Ech - o o'er, ech - o o'er, ech - o o'er!

Woos the night.
Ech - o o'er!

p (closed lips)

Soft, low tone, Woos the night.
Soft, low tone, Ech - o o'er!

cresc.   mp   p   pp

BEDOUIN LOVE SONG

Bayard Taylor

Ciro Pinsuti
Four-part arr.

1. From the des-ert   I come to   thee   On my
2. From thy win-dow . . look and   see . . . . . My

A - rab shod   with   fire,   And   the
pas - sion and   my   pain!   I . .

winds   are left be - hind . .   In the   speed of   my   de - sire.
lie on   the sand be - low, . .   And I   faint in   thy   dis- dain.

Un - der thy win - dow . I stand, . . . And the mid - night hears my
Let . the night winds touch thy brow . . With the breath of my burn - ing

cry, . . . I love thee, I love but thee With a love that shall not
sigh . . . And melt thee to hear the vow Of a love that shall not

die, With a love that shall not die, ...
die, Of a love that shall not die, ...

Till the sun grows

Without Pedal

And the leaves of the Judg - ment . . Book, the Judgment Book un-fold. . .

And the leaves of the Judg - ment . . Book, Book un - fold. . .

THE SONG OF THE IMMIGRANT
(Complete without Bass)

Margaret J. McElroy   E. W. Johns

Andante con moto ♩= 92   Soprano Solo

1. I'm wea - ry for the   old home, lad, The home a - cross the
2. Ah, weel I ken the   chil - lin' blast, That blows a - cross the
3. Ye tell me this maun be my home, Ah, lad, it can - na'

RULE, BRITANNIA!

James Thomson

Dr. Thomas Augustine Arne

1. When Britain first, . . at Heav'n's command, A - rose . . . . . from out the
2. The mus - es, still . . with free - dom found, Shall to . . . . . . thy hap - py

az - ure main, A - rose from out, a - rose from out the az - ure main,
coast . re - pair: Shall to thy hap - py coast, thy hap - py coast re - pair.

This was the char - ter, the char - ter of the land, And guard-ian, guard-ian an - gels
Blest, blest Isle with match - less beau - ty crown'd And man - ly, man - ly hearts to

sang this strain: "Rule, Bri - tan - nia! Bri - tan - nia, rule the waves;
guard the fair. "Rule, Bri - tan - nia! Bri - tan - nia, rule the waves;

Bri - tons nev -er, nev - er, nev - er will be slaves." Rule, Bri - tan - nia! Bri -

SOPR. 2

Rule, Bri - tan - nia! Bri -

ALTO

Rule, Bri - tan - nia! Bri -

BASS

tan - nia, rule the waves; Bri - tons nev - er, nev - er, nev - er will be slaves!"

tan - nia, rule the waves; Bri - tons nev - er, nev - er, nev - er will be slaves!"

tan - nia, rule the waves; Bri - tons nev - er, nev - er, nev - er will be slaves!"

BEYOND THE SPANISH MAIN

Alfred Noyes*

E. W. Johns

Allegro moderato ♩ = 108

Solo (or Unison)

1. The moon is up:. . . the stars are bright :. The
2. We're sick of all . . . the cring - ing knees, . . The
3. Be - yond the light . . of far Cath - ay, . . . Be -

wind is fresh . . and free! . . . . We're out to seek for
court - ly smiles . and lies! . . . . God, let thy sing - ing
yond all mor - tal dreams. . . . Be - yond the reach of

gold to - night A - cross the . sil - ver sea! . . . .
Chan - nel breeze . Light - en our hearts and eyes! . . . .
night and day Our El Do - ra - do gleams, . . .

Chorus

The world was grow-ing grey and old; Break out the sails a-
Let love no more be bought and sold For earth-ly loss or
Re-veal -ing—as the skies un-fold— A star with-out a

(Optional Alto)

The world was grow-ing grey and old; Break out the sails a-
Let love no more be bought and sold For earth-ly loss or
Re-veal -ing—as the skies un-fold— A star with-out a

gain! We're out to seek a Realm of Gold Be-
gain; We're out to seek an Age of Gold Be-
stain, The glo-ry of the Gates of Gold Be-

gain! We're out to seek a Realm of Gold Be-
gain; We're out to seek an Age of Gold Be-
stain, The glo-ry of the Gates of Gold Be-

yond the Span-ish Main. . . .

yond the Span-ish Main. . . .

TURN YE TO ME

John Wilson (Christopher North)

Old Highland Melody
Arr. by Malcolm Lawson

Andante espressivo ♩ = 96

1. The stars . are shin - ing
sea mew is moan - ing
2. The waves are danc - ing
sea - birds are wail - ing

cheer - i - ly, cheer - i - ly, Ho - ro Mhai - ri dhu, turn ye . . to
drear - i - ly, drear - i - ly, (Ma - ry dear,)
mer - ri - ly, mer - ri - ly, Ho - ro Mhai - ri dhu, turn ye . . to
wea - ri - ly, wea - ri - ly,

*In the absence of basses, this melody may be sung by altos

più animato
SOPRANOS

mf

me ; The me. Cold is the storm - wind that ruf - fles his
me ; The me. Hushed be thy moan - ing, lone bird of the

mp

breast, But warm are the down - y plumes lin - ing his nest,
sea, Thy home on the rocks is a shel - ter to thee. Thy

mf   *p*   *tenderly*

Cold blows the storm . there, Soft falls the snow . . there, Ho - ro
home is the an - gry wave, Mine but the lone - ly grave, Ho - ro

rit.   *D.C.*

Mhai - ri dhu, turn ye . . to me.
(Ma - ry, dear,)
Mhai - ri dhu, turn ye . . to me.

D.C.

rit.   *dim.*

O GOD OF LOVE!

Henry W. Baker

Henry W. Baker

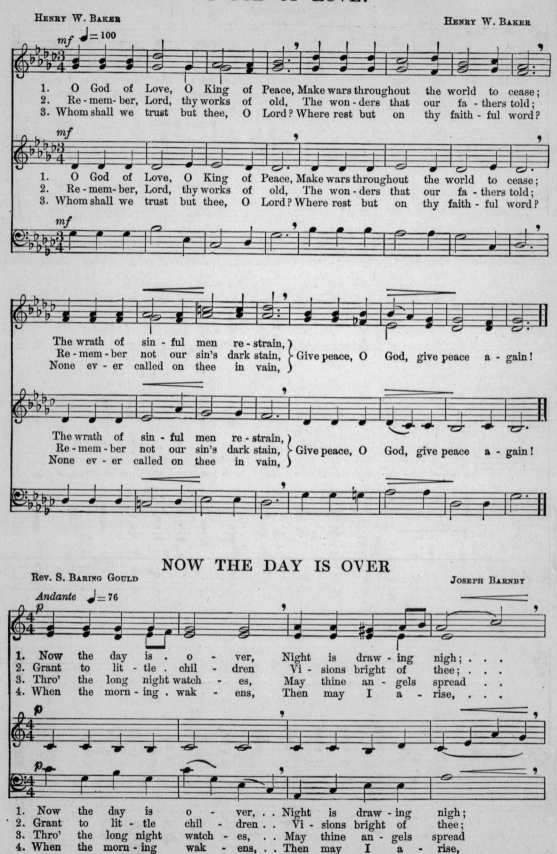

1. O God of Love, O King of Peace, Make wars throughout the world to cease;
2. Re - mem - ber, Lord, thy works of old, The won - ders that our fa - thers told;
3. Whom shall we trust but thee, O Lord? Where rest but on thy faith - ful word?

The wrath of sin - ful men re - strain, ⎫
Re - mem - ber not our sin's dark stain, ⎬ Give peace, O God, give peace a - gain!
None ev - er called on thee in vain, ⎭

NOW THE DAY IS OVER

Rev. S. Baring Gould

Joseph Barnby

Andante ♩ = 76

1. Now the day is . o - ver, Night is draw - ing nigh; . . . .
2. Grant to lit - tle . chil - dren Vi - sions bright of thee; . . . .
3. Thro' the long night watch - es, May thine an - gels spread . . .
4. When the morn - ing . wak - ens, Then may I a - rise, ...

1. Now the day is o - ver, . . Night is draw - ing nigh;
2. Grant to lit - tle chil - dren . . Vi - sions bright of thee;
3. Thro' the long night watch - es, . . May thine an - gels spread
4. When the morn - ing wak - ens, . . Then may I a - rise,

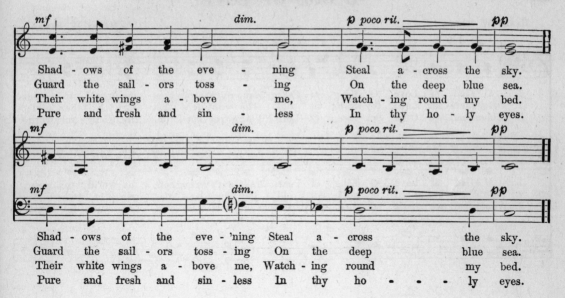

Shad - ows of the eve - ning Steal a - cross the sky.
Guard the sail - ors toss - ing On the deep blue sea.
Their white wings a - bove me, Watch - ing round my bed.
Pure and fresh and sin - less In thy ho - ly eyes.

Shad - ows of the eve - 'ning Steal a - cross the sky.
Guard the sail - ors toss - ing On the deep blue sea.
Their white wings a - bove me, Watch - ing round my bed.
Pure and fresh and sin - less In thy ho - - - ly eyes.

OUR NATIVE LAND

From the Norwegian of   EDVARD GRIEG
NORDAHL ROLFSEN

Grandioso ♩ = 76

1. O God of Hosts, with thy strong hand Pro - tect the sons of our fair land; Be
2. Thou Lord, de - fend this land of ours, Its smil - ing shores, its moun - tain tow'rs; Thy
3. In truth and light we fain would grow, Thy laws would love, thy word would know; In

thou our shield in war or peace, And guide our steps till life shall cease.
bless - ing on its fu - ture shed Like morn - ing dew when night is fled.
thee we will for aye a - bide, O Lord of all, be thou our guide!

Ped.   *

FRIENDSHIP

WOLFGANG AMADEUS MOZART
From "The Magic Flute"

1. Who treads the path of du - ty, Nor shrinks when hon-or
2. Who deep at heart would cher - ish Rude scorn or bit - ter

calls, Fills life with no - ble beau - ty, And ne'er re - treats nor falls;
hate, Who'd see an - oth - er per - ish, And joy . to view his fate;

His steps the voice with - in . . . him leads . .
Not such with-in . our ranks . . is found; .

By gen - tle
Here, friend-ly

paths to gen - tle deeds, . And guides him sure-ly on his way, How-ev- er
cheer and help . . a - bound, . Each oth-er's fail-ings we for - give, And thus in

sad or . . dark the day, And guides him sure - ly on his way, . How - ev - er
peace and . con - cord live, Each oth - er's fail - ings we for - give, And thus in

legato

sad or . . dark the day.
peace and . con - cord live.

p

LIFE'S MIRROR

Mary Alinge de Vere

John E. West

Andante marziale ♩ = 100

Solo (or Semi-Chorus)

mf

1. There are loy - al . . hearts, there are
2. Give . love, and . love to your
3. Give . truth. and your gift will be

mf   *dim.*   *p*

Ped.   *

Ped.   *

spir - its brave, There are souls that are pure . . and true. . . . . Then .
life will flow, A . . strength in its ut - most need. . . . . . Have .
paid in kind, And . hon - or will hon - or meet; . . . . And a

PART FOUR

SOPRANO, ALTO, AND BASS

CHIEF OF THE ARAB BAND

Paul Bliss   Paul Bliss

1. Ah! . . . . . Foot loose!
2. Ah! . . . . . He knows!
3. Ah! . . . . . Twi - light!

1. Foot loose in the
2. I know the o -
3. Oft - times in the

Car - bine on his back, the A - rab chief, o - ver the des - ert!
Wav - ing palm trees grow, the A - rab chief knows hid-den val - leys!
By the tent, at rest, the A - rab chief there in the star - light!

stir-rup, With car - bine on my back; Out o - ver the des - ert To
a - ses Where wav - ing palm-trees grow. I know hid-den val - leys Where
twi-light Be - side my tent, at rest; Dream - ing in the star-light, Fierce

* Unchanged voices may sing this melody.

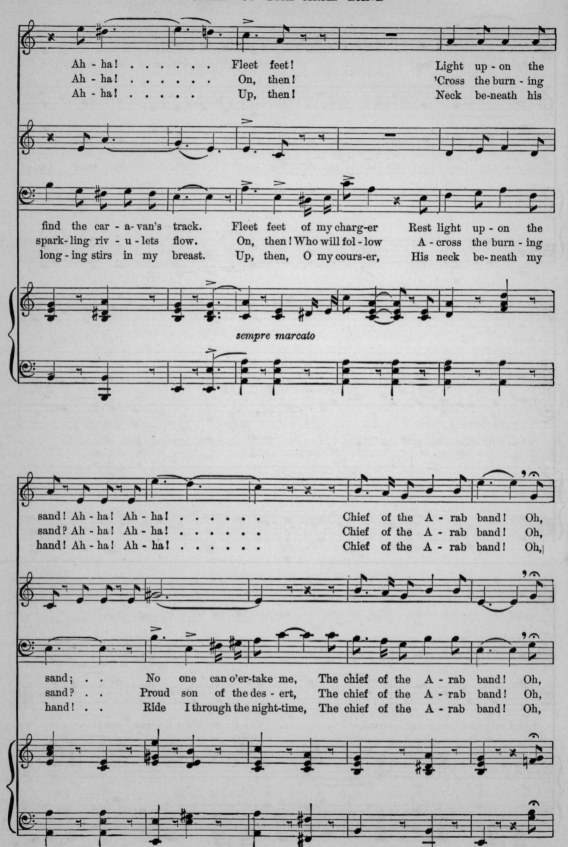

sempre marcato

Ah - ha! . . . . Fleet feet! Light up - on the
Ah - ha! . . . . . . On, then! 'Cross the burn - ing
Ah - ha! . . . . . Up, then! Neck be-neath his

find the car - a - van's track. Fleet feet of my charg-er Rest light up - on the
spark-ling riv - u - lets flow. On, then! Who will fol - low A-cross the burn - ing
long - ing stirs in my breast. Up, then, O my cours-er, His neck be-neath my

sand! Ah - ha! Ah - ha! . . . . . . Chief of the A - rab band! Oh,
sand? Ah - ha! Ah - ha! . . . . . . Chief of the A - rab band! Oh,
hand! Ah - ha! Ah - ha! . . . . . . Chief of the A - rab band! Oh,

sand; . . No one can o'er-take me, The chief of the A - rab band! Oh,
sand? . . Proud son of the des - ert, The chief of the A - rab band! Oh,
hand! . . Ride I through the night-time, The chief of the A - rab band! Oh,

THE OLD MAN CLOTHED IN LEATHER

Mother Goose

SOLO (OR UNISON)

J. W. ELLIOTT
Three-part arr.

1. One mist - y, moist - y morn - ing When cloud - y was the weath - er, O
2. I shook his hand at part - ing, Tho' cloud - y was the weath - er, This

there I met an old man, } Cloth-ed all in leath - er, Cloth- ed all in leath - er, With
im - be -cile old par - ty }

cap un - der his chin. { O how d'ye do, and how d'ye do, And how d'ye do a - gain?
{ O fare thee well, and fare thee well, And fare thee well a - gain!

O how d'ye do, And how d'ye do a - gain?
O fare thee well, And fare thee well a - gain!

Old Tune
Three-part arr.

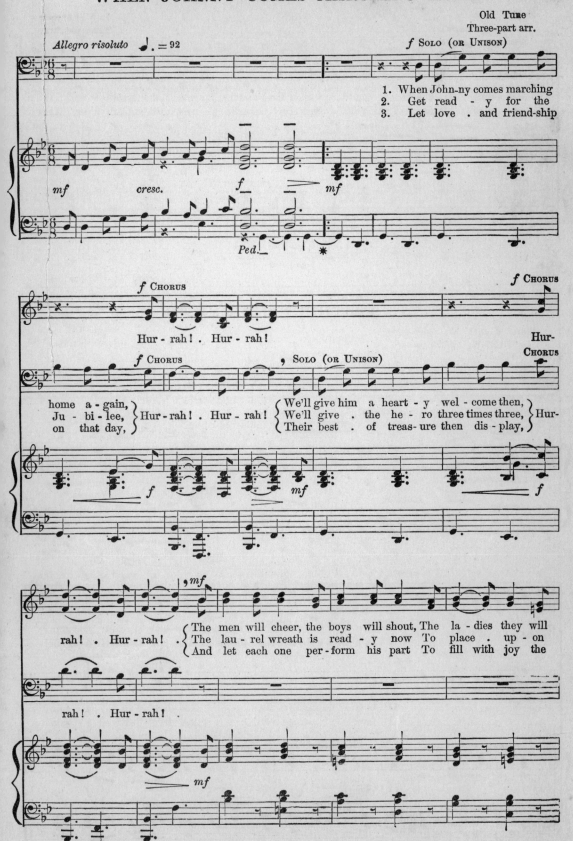

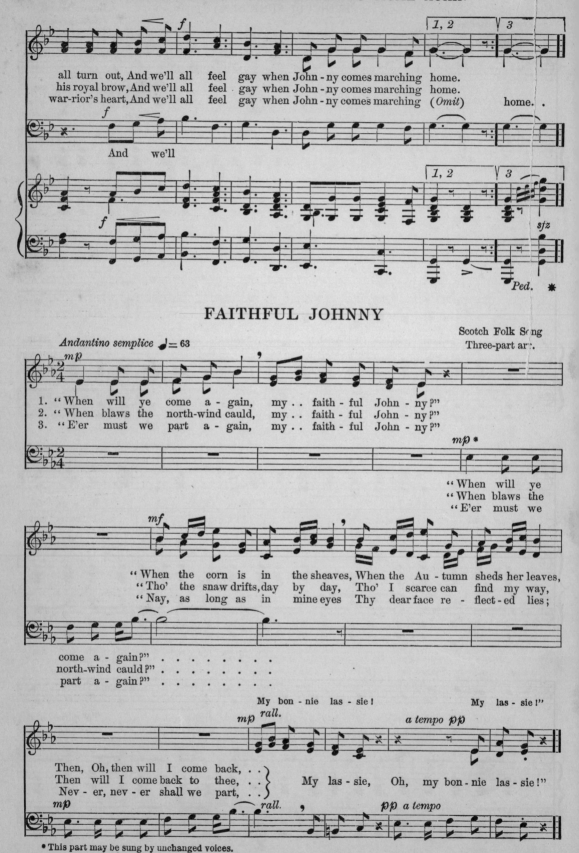

all turn out, And we'll all feel gay when John-ny comes marching home.
his royal brow, And we'll all feel gay when John-ny comes marching home.
war-rior's heart, And we'll all feel gay when John-ny comes marching (Omit) home...

And we'll

FAITHFUL JOHNNY

Scotch Folk Song
Three-part arr.

Andantino semplice ♩ = 63

1. "When will ye come a - gain, my .. faith - ful John - ny?"
2. "When blaws the north-wind cauld, my .. faith - ful John - ny?"
3. "E'er must we part a - gain, my .. faith - ful John - ny?"

"When will ye
"When blaws the
"E'er must we

"When the corn is in the sheaves, When the Au - tumn sheds her leaves,
"Tho' the snaw drifts, day by day, Tho' I scarce can find my way,
"Nay, as long as in mine eyes Thy dear face re - flect - ed lies;

come a - gain?" . . . .
north-wind cauld?" . . . .
part a - gain?" . . . .

My bon - nie las - sie! My las - sie!"

Then, Oh, then will I come back, . .⎫
Then will I come back to thee, . .⎬ My las - sie, Oh, my bon-nie las-sie!"
Nev - er, nev - er shall we part, . .⎭

* This part may be sung by unchanged voices.

A MERRY LIFE
(FUNICULI FUNICULA)

From the Italian

Luigi Denza
Three-part arr.

Refrain

Hark - en' Hark - en! Mu - sic sounds a - far! . . Hark - en! Hark - en!

Mu - sic sounds a - far! Tra - la - la - la, tra - la - la - la, tra - la - la - la, tra - la - la - la!

Joy is ev - 'ry-where, Tra - la - la - la, tra - la - la - la.

CASTLES IN THE AIR

(COMPLETE WITHOUT BASS)

HARVEY WORTHINGTON LOOMIS

ARTHUR EDWARD JOHNSTONE

1. 'Twas on an eve of white De - cem-ber When all the world with frost was fair, I knelt be -
2. 'Tis ev - er spring in those do - min-ions My fan - cy paints with col - ors rare, And hov - ers

side the glow - ing em - ber And build - ed cas - tles in the air; A win - ter
peace with snow - y pin - ions A - bove my cas - tles in the air; A mag - ic

lull - a - by thro' the pine - tree Was soft - ly woo - ing me with its croon; *p* O gen - tle
pic - ture-book is the fire-place, Of what it con-jures up who could tire? *f* As bright as

A LIFE ON THE OCEAN WAVE

EPES—SARGENT

HENRY RUSSELL
Three-part arr.

1. A life on the o-cean wave, . . A . home on the roll-ing
2. Once more on the deck I stand, . . On my own . . swift glid-ing

MELODY *

deep . . . Where the scat-tered wa-ters rave . . And the winds their rev-els
craft; . . Set the sail; fare-well to land! . . The gale fol-lows far . a-

deep! . . .
keep! . . Like an ea-gle caged, I pine . . On this dull, un-chang-ing
baft. . . Shoot-ing thro' the spark-ling foam . . Like an o-cean bird set

Yo, heave ho, yo ho! Yo, heave

shore, . . . Oh, . give me the flash-ing brine, . . The spray and the tem - pest
free, . . Like the o - cean bird our home . . We'll find . far out on the

ho, yo ho! O - - - - cean home, . . . the roll - - - - - ing

roar! . . . A life on the o-cean wave, . . A home on the roll-ing
sea. . . .

deep, Yo ho!

deep, . . Where the scat-tered wa-ters rave . . And the winds their rev - els keep.

* Bass or Alto

Shep-herds, have you seen, tell me have you seen my Flo - ra pass this way?

tell me, have you seen, tell me have you seen my Flo - ra pass this way?

Shep-herds, have you seen, tell me have you seen my Flo - ra pass this way?

3. The beau - teous, the beauteous wreath that decks, that decks her head, Forms her de -

scrip - tion, her de - scrip-tion true. Hands lil - y white,

Lips crim - son red, And cheeks of ros - y, ros - y . hue.

CORNISH MAY SONG

Sir Alexander Boswell

Tempo giusto ♩ = 76

Old English Morris Dance
Three-part arr.

1. Ye coun - try maid - ens, gath - er dew While yet the morn-ing breez - es blow;
2. With song and dance, in fes - tive band, Each hap - py lad may lead his lass;
3. Or from the thick - et in the glade Go pluck with speed the haw-thorn bough,

Then cau - tious mark them as ye go,
O'er ev - 'ry thresh-old free - ly pass.
Who has thy troth and plight-ed vow,

The fair - y rings are fresh and new,. . . . . O ho!
With mirth- ful smiles, and hand in hand,. . . . . O ho!
And twine a wreath to deck the maid,. . . . . O ho!

(*divide*)

Then cau - tious as ye go!
For - got - ten Flo - ra Day.
Who has thy plight- ed vow.

Refrain

A - rise, a - rise, the night is past, The sky - lark hails the dawn of day;

For mirth rules here, this morn of May.

Care, get thee hence, from this place, fly!. . . . . O ho!

(*divide*)

For mirth rules here, this morn.

* Without variation of tempo.

SISTER MONTHS

Frederick Winthrop

Arthur Edward Johnstone

1. May-time, O the sweet and ver-nal May-time at the hour of dawn! 'Tis then all things
2. June-tide, O the soft and scent-ed June-tide when the ros-es bloom! There's gold in the

May-time, O the mild and fra-grant
June-tide, O the lan-g'rous hours of

blos-som out, and the bob-o-link trills his note. . . . .
lil-y-bed tho' the daf-fo-dil days are o'er. . . . .

May-time when the wood-land wakes, And songs out of fair-y-land by the
June-tide that en-tice the heart And life seems but hol-i-day with a

Songs o'er . . . the
Life seems . . . to

A CAPITAL SHIP

English Tune
Three-part arr.

Allegro giocoso ♩ = 100 *f* Solo (or Unison)

1. A cap - i - tal ship for an o - cean trip Was the
2. The bo' - swain's mate was . ver - y se - date, Yet .
3. The cap - tain sat on the com-mo-dore's hat, And .
4. All nau - ti - cal pride we . laid . a - side, And we
5. On Rug - bug bark, from . morn till dark, We .

Wal - lop - ing . . Win - dow Blind! No . . wind . that blew dis -
fond . of a - muse - ment too; He . . played hop - scotch with the
dined in a roy - al way, Off . . toast - ed pigs and .
ran . the . ves - sel a - shore On the Gul - li - by Isles where the
dined . till we all . . had grown Un - com - mon - ly shrunk, when a

mayed her crew, Or . trou-bled the cap - tain's mind. The man at the wheel was
star-board watch, While the cap - tain tickled the crew. And the gun-ner we . had was ap -
pick-les and figs, And gun-ner-y . bread each day. And the cook was Dutch and be -
Poo - poo smiles, And the rub - bly . Ub - dugs roar. And we sat . on the edge of a
Chi - nese junk Came up . from the Tor-ri - bly zone. She was chub-by and square, but we

made to feel Con - tempt for the wild - est blow - ow - ow, Tho' it
par - ent - ly mad, For he sat on the aft - er rai - ai - ail, And .
haved as such, For the di - et he gave the crew - ew - ew, Was a
sand - y ledge And . shot at the whis - tling bee - ee - ee; And the
did - n't much care, So we cheer - i - ly put out to sea - ee - ee; And we

of - ten ap - peared, when the gale . had cleared, That he'd been in his bunk be - low.
fired . sa - lutes with the cap - tain's boots, In the teeth of the boom - ing gale!
num - ber of tons of . . hot . . cross buns Served up with . sug - ar and glue.
cin - na - mon bats wore . wa - ter - proof hats As they dipped in the shin - y sea.
left all the crew of the junk . to chew On the bark of the Rug - bug tree.

CHORUS

Then blow, ye winds, heigh ho! A - rov - ing I will go! I'll

stay no more on Eng-land's shore, So let the mu-sic play-ay-ay! I'm

off for the morn-ing train! I'll cross the rag-ing main! I'm

off to my love with a box-ing-glove, Ten thou-sand miles a-way!

FOR FREEDOM

KATHARINE WHITMORE

(COMPLETE WITHOUT ALTO)

SIR ARTHUR SULLIVAN

From "Iolanthe"

Allegro moderato ♩ = 84

BASS SOLO (OR UNISON)

1. When bu-gles play, when drums are beat, When sounds the call to arms, From
2. 'Mid shriek of shell and blast of gun Each heart must brave his fate, 'Twere

moun-tain-side, from crowd-ed street Our val-iant sons the sum-mons meet, Nor
not a-lone who've vic-t'ry won, But those who no-blest deeds have done, That

blench at war's a-larms. A pledge of un-ion stirs the breast, Glad mu-sic to the
lau-rel wreaths a-wait. That truth and jus-tice ne'er shall die, We raise a-gain our

earth's oppressed, The song that ech-oed round the world When Freedom's flag was first un-furled.
bat-tle-cry, The song that ech-oed round the world When Freedom's flag was first un-furled.

Chorus

The song that ech - oed round the world When Free-dom's flag was first un-furled.

(OPTIONAL ALTO)

The song that ech - oed round the world When Free-dom's flag was first un-furled!

THE RAGGLE-TAGGLE GYPSIES

Traditional (abridged)   Somerset Folk Tune
                                                Three-part arr.

Allegro moderato ♩ = 72

1. There .. were three gyp - sies a - come to my door, And
2. It was late last night when my lord came .. home, En -

(BASS MELODY)

down - stairs ran this a - la - dy, O! . . . One sang high and the
quir - ing for his a - la - dy, O! The ser - vants said on . .

oth - er sang low, And the oth - er sang "Bon - ny, Bon - ny Bis - cay, O!"
ev - 'ry hand, "She's gone . with the rag - gle - tag - gle gyp - sies, O!"

W. E. Hickson

Dr. Callcott
Three-part arr.

Allegretto ♩ = 72

1. May ev - 'ry year But draw more near The time when strife shall cease, And
2. Let good men ne'er Of truth des - pair Tho' hum - ble ef - forts fail, Not

truth and love All hearts shall move To live in joy and peace. Now sor - row reigns, And
e'er give o'er Un - til once more The righteous cause pre - vail. In vain, and long, En -

earth com-plains, For fol - ly still her pow'r main-tains. But the day shall yet ap - pear
dur - ing wrong, The weak may strive a - gainst the strong, But the day shall sure-ly come

The right . . . .

When the might with the right and the truth shall be, the right . . . . with the

(*divide*)

When the might and the right

truth shall be, And come what may To stand in the way, That day the world shall see.

A SONG OF LIGHT AND PRAISE

James F. Caldwell

Arthur Edward Johnstone

1. Stars bring the night a mem'ry of the day;
2. God lights the stars, the plan-ets, and the sun;

1. Seek ye the light, that wan-der in the dark-ness, and find the heav'n - born ray;
2. Praise be to God who giv-eth us the light of the stars, the moon, the sun;

Larks in their flight have shown the az - ure
God wakes the birds ere morn-ing is be-

Seek ye the light, nor tar-ry in the shades of the twi - light gray; Seek . .
Praise be to God who giv-eth us the joy . . of the wood - bird's song; Praise . .

way; God in his might be-stows the sun-ny ray.
gun; Praise be to God for all his love has done.

. . ye the light, all ye that walk in dark-ness, and bask in the heav'n - born ray.
. . be to God who show-eth forth his light and his love un - to ev - 'ry one.

M. F. Butts
From "The Youth's Companion"

E. W. Johns

1. A jol-ly fel-low is young March Wind With all his blus- -ter and noise; Tho' he has no thought for the old and poor, He's a thor-ough friend . . . of the boys. A-ha, . . . a-ha, . . . a-ha, . . . a-ha, . . . He joins their play with right good will, A-ha, d'you see him go, . . . With a hi, hi, . hi, Far . up in the sky, While the boys stand tug-ging be-low.

2. Oh, a nois-y fel-low is young March Wind, And al-most an-y day You may see him up in the high-est trees . . Blow-ing his trump-et for play. O-ho! . . o-ho! . . o-ho, . . o-ho! . . O-ho! o-ho! now high, now low, He blows with all his might;. . . Oh, . dear Mis-ter Wind, Would you be so . kind As to go to sleep at night?

ROW, ROW, ROW YOUR BOAT
(ROUND)

E. O. Lyte

Row, row, row your boat Gen-tly down the stream;

Mer-ri-ly, mer-ri-ly, mer-ri-ly, mer-ri-ly, Life is but a dream.

THE HAMMER SONG

George F. Root
Three-part arr.

1. To the noise of the an-vil's ring-ing, And the
2. To the fire of the for-ge's glanc-ing, And the

(Divide) Clang, clang, clang, clang, clang, clang, clang, clang,

Cling, cling, cling, cling, cling, cling, cling, cling,

voice of the sharp steel sing-ing, } Join the song, (cling, clang) mer-ry
stars of the i-ron danc-ing, }

clang, clang, clang, Mer-ry song!

cling, cling, cling, cling,

song, (cling, clang,) Of the ham-mer blow so clear and strong. Join the
Mer-ry song! The blow so strong, cling, clang,

song, (cling, clang,) mer-ry song, (cling, clang,) Of the ham-mer blow so clear and strong.
Mer-ry song! Mer-ry song! The blow so strong, cling, clang.

WINTER ROSES

Harvey Worthington Loomis

Herbert Fullerton

1. With frost . . . up-on the air, ... I
2. I looked; . . 'twas deep in snow— . . . My

1. One drear-y win-ter twi-light, With frost up-on the air, . . . I
2. I looked a-gain at dawn-ing, The gar-den deep in snow— . . My

(Bass Melody)

looked at my white-rose . vine, All blos-som-less and bare. .
vine had whit-er ros- es . . Than ev-er June can show. .

LONG, LONG AGO

(COMPLETE WITHOUT BASS)

T. H. BAYLY

T. H. BAYLY
Three-part arr.

1. Tell me the tales that to me were so dear,
2. Do you re-mem-ber the path where we met
3. Though by your kind-ness my fond hopes were raised
} Long, long a - go, Long, long a - go,

Sing me the songs I de-light-ed to hear,
Ah, yes, you told me you ne'er would for-get,
You, by more el - o - quent lips have been praised,
} Long, long a - go, long a - go.

Now you have come, all my grief is re-moved, Let me for-get that so long you have roved,
Then to all oth - ers my smile you pre-ferred, Love when you spoke gave a charm to each word,
But by long ab-sence your truth has been tried, Still to your ac - cents I list - en with pride,

Long, long a - go,   Long, long a - go,

Let me be - lieve that you love as you loved,
Still my heart treas-ures the prais - es I heard,
Blest as I was when I sat by your side,
} Long, long a - go, long a - go.

COME, SOUND HIS PRAISE

(COMPLETE WITHOUT BASS)

ISAAC WATTS

ISAAC SMITH

Risoluto ♩ = 76

1. Come, sound his praise a - broad, And hymns of glo - ry .. sing: Je -
2. He formed the deeps, un - known; He gave the seas . their . bound; The

ho - vah is the sov - 'reign. God, The u - - ni - ver - sal King.
wa - t'ry worlds are all . his .. own, And all . . . the sol - id ground.

JUANITA *
(COMPLETE WITHOUT BASS)

CAROLINE NORTON

Spanish Melody

Moderato ♩ = 80

1. Soft o'er the foun - tain Ling - 'ring falls the south - ern moon;
2. When in thy dream - ing, Moons like these shall shine a - gain,

Far o'er the moun - tain Breaks the day too . . soon!
And, day - light beam - ing, Prove thy dreams are . . vain,

In thy dark eyes' splen - dor, Where the warm light loves to dwell,
Wilt thou not, re - lent - ing, For thine ab - sent lov - er sigh,

Wea - ry looks, yet ten - der, Speak their fond fare - well.
In thy heart con - sent - ing To a prayer gone by?

REFRAIN

Ni - ta, Juan - i - ta!* Ask thy soul if we should part!
Ni - ta, Juan - i - ta! Let me lin - ger by thy side!

molto ritard.

Ni - ta, Juan - i - ta! Lean thou on my heart!
Ni - ta, Juan - i - ta! Be my own fair bride!
molto ritard.

* Pronounce hwah-nee-tah.

PART FIVE

COMMUNITY SONGS AND HYMNS

AMERICA

Samuel Francis Smith

Henry Carey

1. My coun - try, 'tis of thee, Sweet land of lib - er - ty,
2. My na - tive coun - try, thee — Land of the no - ble free,
3. Let mu - sic swell the breeze, And ring from all the trees
4. Our fa - thers' God! to thee, Au - thor of lib - er - ty,

Of thee I sing; Land where my fa - thers died; Land of the
Thy name I love; I love thy rocks and rills, Thy woods and
Sweet free - dom's song; Let mor - tal tongues a - wake; Let all that
To thee we sing; Long may our land be bright With free - dom's

cres - - cen - - do

Pil - grims' pride! From ev - 'ry . moun - tain-side Let free - dom ring!
tem - pled hills; My heart with rap - ture thrills Like that a - bove.
breathe par - take; Let rocks their si - lence break, The sound pro - long.
ho - ly light; Pro - tect us . by thy might, Great God, our King!

AMERICA THE BEAUTIFUL

Katharine Lee Bates*

Samuel A. Ward
Arr. for this work

TENTING TO-NIGHT

WALTER KITTREDGE   WALTER KITTREDGE
Moderato ♩= 92

1. We're tent-ing to-night on the old camp-ground, Give us a song to cheer. Our.
2. We've been tent-ing to-night on the old camp-ground, Think-ing of days gone by;.. Of the

wea-ry . .hearts; a song of . . home And . friends we love so dear.
lov'd ones at home that gave us the hand, And the tear that said "Good-bye."

REFRAIN

Man-y are the hearts that are wea-ry to-night, Wish-ing for the war to cease;..

Man-y are the hearts that are look-ing for the right, To see the dawn of peace.

Tent-ing to-night, Tent-ing to-night, Tent-ing on the old camp-ground.

Tent-ing to-night, Tent-ing to-night,

LOVE'S OLD, SWEET SONG

G. Clifton Bingham

J. L. Molloy

1. Once in the dear, dead days be-yond re-call, When on the world the
2. E-ven to-day we hear Love's song of yore, Deep in our hearts it

mists be-gan to fall, Out of the dreams that rose in hap-py throng
dwells for-ev-er-more, Foot-steps may fal-ter, wea-ry grow the way,

Low to our hearts Love sang an old sweet song; And in the dusk where
Still we can hear it at the close of day; So till the end, when

frost - y morn-in';
for - ty-pound-er;
broke her heart; Look a - way! Look a - way! Look a - way! Dix - ie Land.
song to-mor-row;
bound to trab-ble;

REFRAIN

Den I wish I was in Dix - ie, Hoo-ray! Hoo-ray! In . Dix-ie Land I'll

Ped. * Ped. *

take my stand To lib and die in Dix - ie. A - way, a - way, A -

way down south in Dix - ie; A - way, a - way, A - way down south in Dix - ie.

VIRGINIA VERSION *etc.*

1. { I wish I was in de lan' ob cot - ton—Old times dere is not for-got-ten,
   { 'Tis dere we pass'd such pleas-ant hours 'Mid de for - es' leaves an' flow'rs, } Look a - way! etc.

2. { O gay de times we had to - ged-der; Cared not we for wind or wed-der,
   { 'Twas al-ways gay and pleas-ant dere; Ne'er a cloud and ne'er a care, } Look a - way! etc.

OLD HUNDREDTH

Rev. Isaac Watts

Louis Bourgeois
From The Geneva Psalter (1551)

1. E - ter - nal are thy mer - cies, Lord; E - ter - nal truth at - tends thy word;
2. Praise God from whom all bless - ings flow; Praise him, all crea - tures here be - low;

Thy praise shall sound from shore to shore, Till suns shall rise and set no more.
Praise him, ye heav'n - ly host a - bove, Praise him, my soul, for all his love.

Mrs. Jordan

Scotch Folk Song

Allegretto ♩ = 60

1. Oh, where and Oh, where is your High-land lad-die gone? Oh, where and Oh,
2. Oh, where and Oh, where did your High-land lad-die dwell? Oh, where and Oh,
3. What clothes, in what clothes is your High-land lad-die clad? What clothes, in what
4. Sup-pose, and sup-pose that your High-land lad should die? Sup-pose, and sup-

where is your High-land lad-die gone? He's gone to fight the foe for King
where did your High-land lad-die dwell? He dwelt in mer-ry Scot-land at the
clothes is your High-land lad-die clad? His bon-net's Sax-on green and his
pose that your High-land lad should die? The bag-pipes shall play o'er him, I'd

George up-on the throne, And it's Oh, in my heart, I wish him safe at home!
sign of the Blue Bell; And it's Oh, in my heart, I love my lad-die well.
waist-coat of the plaid; And it's Oh, in my heart, I love my High-land lad.
lay me down and cry; And it's Oh, in my heart, I wish he may not die.

And it's Oh, it's Oh, . . .

(divide)

ANNIE LAURIE

Douglas of Fingland

Scotch Melody
Arr. for this work

Andante con moto ♩ = 84

1. Max - wel - ton's braes   are bon - nie,   Where ear - ly fa's the .
2. Her   brow . is like   the snaw - drift,   Her . throat   is like   the .
3. Like dew on the gow - an ly - ing   Is the fa' o' her fair - y . .

dew,   And it's there that An - nie Lau - rie   Gie'd me   her prom - ise true;
swan,   Her   face   it is the fair - est   That e'er   the sun shone on;
feet;   Like winds in sum - mer sigh - ing,   Her voice   is low and sweet;

Gie'd   me   her   prom - ise true,   Which   ne'er   for - got   will   be;
That   e'er   the   sun   shone   on,   And .   dark   blue   is   her   ee;
Her   voice   is   low   and   sweet,   And she's a'   the   world   to   me;

And for bon-nie An-nie Lau-rie I'd .. lay . me doune and dee.

And for bon-nie An-nie Lau-rie I'd . lay me doune and dee.

ALL THROUGH THE NIGHT

From the Welsh   (COMPLETE WITHOUT BASS)   Welsh Folk Tune
Arr. for this work

Andante con moto ♩ = 88

1. Sleep, my child, and peace at-tend thee, All .. through the night;
   Guard-ian an-gels . God will send thee, All .. through the night;
2. Though I roam, a .. min-strel lone-ly, All .. through the night,
   My true harp shall . praise thee on-ly, All .. through the night;
3. Hark! a sol-emn . bell is ring-ing Clear, through the night;
   Thou, my love, art .. heav'n-ward wing-ing, Home, through the night;

Soft the drow-sy hours are creep-ing, Hill and vale in splen-dor steep-ing,
Love's young dream, a-las! is o-ver, Yet my strains of love shall hov-er
Earth-ly dust, from off thee shak-en, Soul im-mor-tal, thou shalt wak-en,

Hours are creep - - ing,
Dream is o - - - ver,
Soul im-mor - - tal,

I my lov-ing . vig-il keep-ing, All .. through the night.
Near the pres-ence . of my lov-er, All .. through the night.
With thy last dim . jour-ney tak-en, All .. through the night.

OLD FOLKS AT HOME

(COMPLETE WITHOUT BASS)

STEPHEN C. FOSTER

STEPHEN C. FOSTER
ARR. for this work

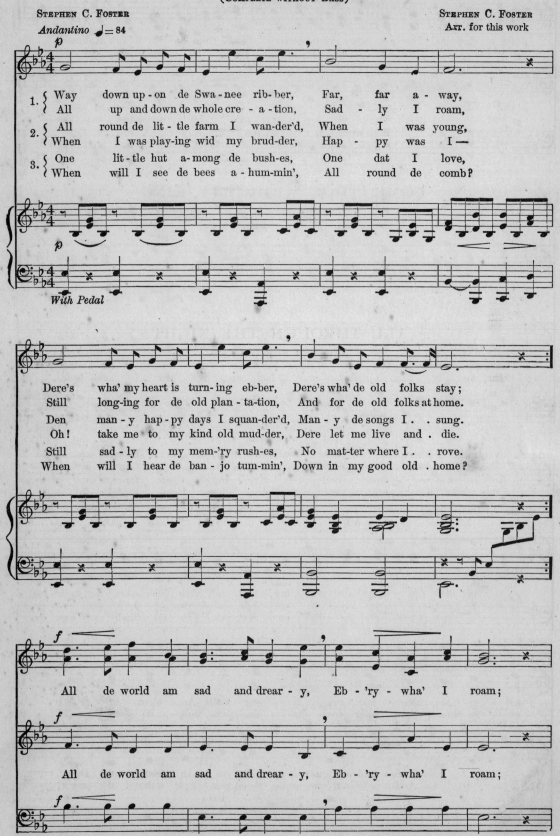

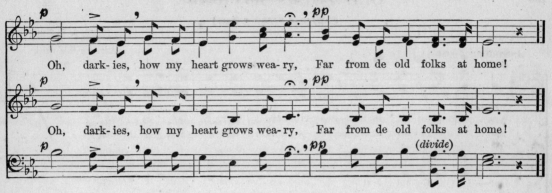

Oh, dark- ies, how my heart grows wea - ry, Far from de old folks at home!

Oh, dark- ies, how my heart grows wea - ry, Far from de old folks at home!

COME, THOU ALMIGHTY KING

CHARLES WESLEY (COMPLETE WITHOUT BASS) FELICE DE GIARDINI
Arr. for this work

Moderato ♩ = 100

1. Come, thou Al - might - y King, Help us thy name . . to sing,
2. Come, ho - ly Com - fort - er, Thy sa - cred wit - ness bear,

1. Come, thou Al - might - y King, Help us thy name . . to sing,
2. Come, ho - ly Com - fort - er, Thy sa - cred wit - ness bear,

Help us to praise! Fa - ther all - glo - ri - ous, O'er all vic -
In this glad hour! Thou who al - might - y art, Now rule in

Help us to praise!
In this glad hour!

to - ri - ous, Come and reign o - ver us, An - cient of Days!
ev - 'ry heart, And ne'er from us de - part, Spir - it of pow'r!

Come and reign o - ver us, An - cient of Days!
And ne'er from us de - part, Spir - it of pow'r!

MUSIC IN THE AIR

(Complete without Bass)

George F. Root
Four-part arr.

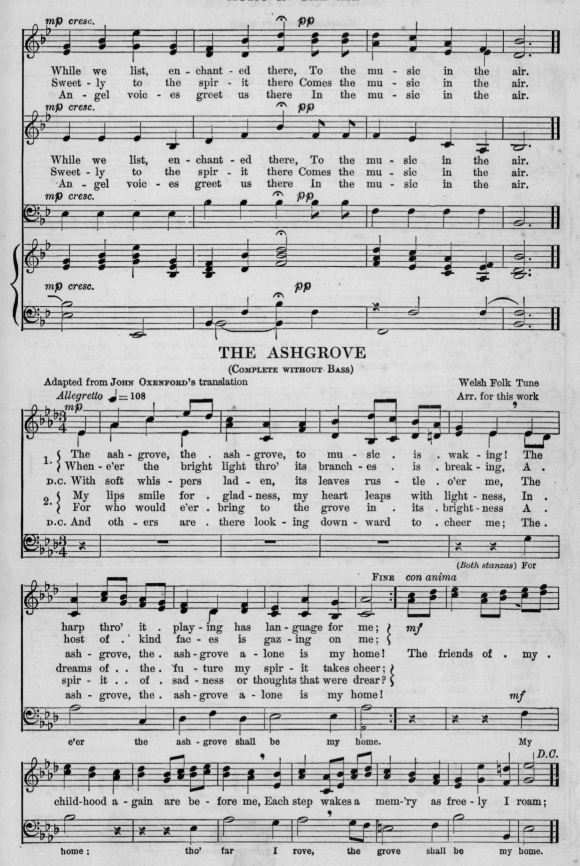

While we list, en-chant-ed there, To the mu-sic in the air.
Sweet-ly to the spir-it there Comes the mu-sic in the air.
An-gel voic-es greet us there In the mu-sic in the air.

While we list, en-chant-ed there, To the mu-sic in the air.
Sweet-ly to the spir-it there Comes the mu-sic in the air.
An-gel voic-es greet us there In the mu-sic in the air.

THE ASHGROVE
(COMPLETE WITHOUT BASS)

Adapted from JOHN OXENFORD's translation

Welsh Folk Tune
Arr. for this work

Allegretto ♩ = 108

1. The ash-grove, the ash-grove, to mu-sic is wak-ing! The
   When-e'er the bright light thro' its branch-es is break-ing, A.
D.C. With soft whis-pers lad-en, its leaves rus-tle o'er me, The

2. My lips smile for glad-ness, my heart leaps with light-ness, In.
   For who would e'er bring to the grove in its bright-ness A.
D.C. And oth-ers are there look-ing down-ward to cheer me; The.

(Both stanzas) For

FINE   con anima

harp thro' it play-ing has lan-guage for me;
host of kind fac-es is gaz-ing on me;
ash-grove, the ash-grove a-lone is my home! The friends of my.
dreams of the fu-ture my spir-it takes cheer;
spir-it of sad-ness or thoughts that were drear?
ash-grove, the ash-grove a-lone is my home!

e'er the ash-grove shall be my home.   My

D.C.

child-hood a-gain are be-fore me, Each step wakes a mem-'ry as free-ly I roam;

home;   tho' far I rove, the grove shall be my home.

MY OLD KENTUCKY HOME
(COMPLETE WITHOUT BASS)

STEPHEN C. FOSTER

STEPHEN C. FOSTER
Arr. for this work

birds make . mu - sic all the day.
bench by the old . . cab - in door;
field where the su - gar canes . . grow;

old Ken - tuck - y home, good night.

REFRAIN

Weep no more, my la - dy, O weep no more to - day! We will sing one song for the

Weep no more, my la - dy, O weep no more to - day! We will sing one song for the

old Ken-tuck - y home, For the old Ken-tuck - y home, far a - way.

old Ken-tuck - y home, For the old Ken-tuck - y home, far a - way.

FLOW GENTLY, SWEET AFTON

(COMPLETE WITHOUT BASS)

ROBERT BURNS

JAMES E. SPILMAN
Arr. for this work

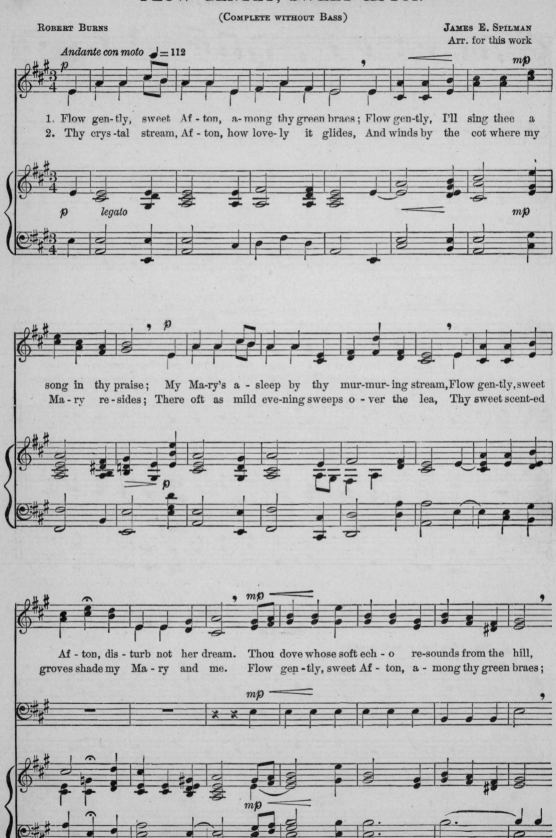

Andante con moto ♩ = 112

1. Flow gen-tly, sweet Af-ton, a-mong thy green braes; Flow gent-ly, I'll sing thee a
2. Thy crys-tal stream, Af-ton, how love-ly it glides, And winds by the cot where my

song in thy praise; My Ma-ry's a-sleep by thy mur-mur-ing stream, Flow gen-tly, sweet
Ma-ry re-sides; There oft as mild eve-ning sweeps o-ver the lea, Thy sweet scent-ed

Af-ton, dis-turb not her dream. Thou dove whose soft ech-o re-sounds from the hill,
groves shade my Ma-ry and me. Flow gen-tly, sweet Af-ton, a-mong thy green braes;

Thou green-crest - ed lap - wing with   noise loud and shrill; Ye wild whist - ling
Flow gen - tly, sweet riv - er, the   theme of my   lays; My Ma - ry's a -

war-blers, your mu - sic for - bear; I charge you dis - turb not the slum - ber - ing fair.
sleep by thy mur-mur - ing stream; Flow gen - tly, sweet Af - ton, dis - turb not her dream.

LOVELY EVENING

ROUND

Oh, how love - ly is the eve - ning, is the eve - ning

When the bells are sweet - ly ring - ing, sweet - ly ring - ing,

Bim, bom, bim, bom, bim, bom.

OLD DOG TRAY
(COMPLETE WITHOUT BASS)

STEPHEN C. FOSTER

STEPHEN C. FOSTER
Arr. for this work

1. The morn of life is past, And eve - ning comes at last; It
2. The forms I call my own Have van - ished one by one, The
3. When thoughts re - call the past, His eyes are on me cast, I

brings me a dream of a once hap - py day, Of mer - ry forms I've seen Up -
loved ones, the dear ones have all passed a - way; The hap - py smiles have flown, Their
know he feels what my breaking heart would say; Al - tho' he can - not speak, I'll

on the vil - lage green, Sport - ing with my old dog Tray.
gen - tle voic - es gone, I've noth - ing left but old dog Tray.
vain - ly, vain - ly seek A bet - ter friend than old dog Tray.

REFRAIN
Con anima

Old dog Tray, ev - er faith - ful; Grief can - not drive him a - way; He's

Old dog Tray, ev - er faith - ful; Grief can - not drive him a - way; He's

OLD DOG TRAY

Tempo primo

gen - tle, he is kind, I'll nev - er, nev - er find A bet - ter friend than old dog Tray.

gen - tle, he is kind, I'll nev - er, nev - er find A bet - ter friend than old dog Tray.

COMIN' THRO' THE RYE

Scotch Folk Song
Arr. for this work

Tempo rubato ♩ = 72

mp

1. If a bod - y meet a bod - y com - in' thro' the rye,
2. If a bod - y meet a bod - y com - in' frae the town,
3. A - mong the train there is a swain I dear - ly love my - sel'; But

If a bod - y kiss a bod - y, need a bod - y cry?
If a bod - y greet a bod - y, need a bod - y frown?
what's his name, or where's his hame, I din - na choose to tell.

mf

Ev - 'ry las - sie has her lad - die, Nane, they say, ha'e I; Yet

When

a' the lads they smile on me, Com - in' thro' the rye.

Thro' the rye.

HOME, SWEET HOME

(COMPLETE WITHOUT BASS)

John Howard Payne

Sir Henry Bishop
Arr. for this work

1. 'Mid pleas - ures and pal - a - ces though . we may roam,   Be it
2. I . gaze . . on the moon   as I tread the drear . . wild,   And .
3. An ex - ile from home, splen - dor daz - zles in vain;   Oh, .

ev - er so hum - ble, there's no . . . place like home; . . A . .
feel . . that my moth - er now thinks . of her child . . As she
give . . me my low - ly thatch'd cot - tage a - gain! . . The .

charm . . from the skies seems to hal - low us there, . . Which
looks . . on that moon from our own . . cot - tage door, . . Thro' the
birds . . . sing - ing gai - ly, that came . at my call, . . . Give me

seek . . thro' the world,   is ne'er met . . with else - where.
wood - bine whose fra - grance shall cheer . me no more.
them . . and that peace   of mind, dear - er than all.

REFRAIN

Home, home, sweet, sweet home, Be it ev - er so hum-ble, There's no place like home.

Home, home, sweet, sweet home, Be it ev - er so hum-ble, There's no place like home.

(divide)

(divide)

MIZPAH

(COMPLETE WITHOUT BASS)

English
Arr. for this work

Tranquillo ♩ = 72

God   be with you till we meet a - gain! What - so - e'er the path be - fore you,

God   be with you till we meet a - gain! What - so - e'er the path be - fore you,

Keep   his bow of prom-ise o'er you; God   be with you till we meet a - gain!

Keep   his bow of prom-ise o'er you; God   be with you till we meet a - gain!

(divide)

COLUMBIA, THE GEM OF THE OCEAN

(Complete without Bass)

David T. Shaw

David T. Shaw
Arr. for this work

Tempo di marcia ♩ = 112

1. O Co-lum-bia! the gem of the o-cean, The home of the brave and the
2. When war wing'd its wide des-o-la-tion, And threat-en'd the land to de-
3. The Star-Span-gled Ban-ner bring hith-er, O'er Co-lum-bia's true sons let it

free, . . . The . shrine of each pa-triot's de-vo-tion, A . .
form, . . . The . ark then of free-dom's foun-da-tion, Co -
wave; . . . May the wreaths they have won nev-er with-er, Nor its

world of-fers hom-age to thee! Thy man-dates make he-roes as-
lum-bia rode safe thro' the storm; With the gar-land of vic-t'ry a-
stars cease to shine on the brave. May the ser-vice u-nit-ed ne'er

sem-ble, When Lib-er-ty's form stands in view; . . . Thy . .
round her, When so proud-ly she bore her brave crew, . . . With her
sev-er, But . hold to their col-ors so true; . . . The . .

ban - ners make tyr - an-ny trem-ble,
flag proud-ly float-ing be - fore her,
Ar - my and Na - vy for - ev - er!

When borne by the red, white, and blue.
The boast of the red, white, and blue.
Three cheers for the red, white, and blue.

CHORUS

When borne by the red, white, and blue, . . When borne by the red, white, and blue, . . Thy . .
The boast of the red, white, and blue, . . The boast of the red, white, and blue, . . With her
Three cheers for the red, white, and blue, . . Three cheers for the red, white, and blue, . . The . .

ban - ners make tyr - an-ny trem-ble,
flag proud-ly float-ing be - fore her,
Ar - my and Na - vy for - ev - er!

When borne by the red, white, and blue.
The boast of the red, white, and blue.
Three cheers for the red, white, and blue.

THE STAR-SPANGLED BANNER

Francis Scott Key

John Stafford Smith
Har. by Arthur Edward Johnstone

Maestoso ♩ = 104

1. O . . say can you see, by the dawn's ear-ly light, What so
2. On the shore, dim-ly seen thro' the mists of the deep, Where the
3. O . . thus be it ev-er when free-men shall stand Be -

proud-ly we hailed at the twi-light's last gleam-ing, Whose broad stripes and bright
foe's haugh-ty host in dread si-lence re-pos-es, What is that which the
tween their lov'd home and the war's des-o-la-tion! Blest with vic-t'ry and

stars, thro' the per-il-ous fight, O'er the ram-parts we watched, were so
breeze, o'er the tow-er-ing steep, As it fit-ful-ly blows, half con-
peace, may the heav'n-res-cued land Praise the pow'r that hath made and pre-

gal-lant-ly stream-ing? And the rock-et's red glare, the bombs burst-ing in
ceals, half dis-clos-es? Now it catch-es the gleam of the morn-ing's first
served us a na-tion! Then . con-quer we must, when our cause it is

ITALIAN TERMS
COMMONLY USED IN MUSIC

Accelerando (ăk-sĕl-ĕr-*än*-dō). Gradually faster.

Ad libitum (äd-*lĭb*-ĭ-tŭm). At pleasure.

Adagio (á-*dä*-jĭō). Slow; leisurely.

Al (äl). To the.

Alla (*äl*-lä). In the style of.

Allargando (äl-lär-*gän*-dō). Slower and with emphasis.

Allegretto (äl-lā-*grĕt*-tō). Slower than *Allegro*.

Allegro (äl-*lā*-grō). Quick; lively.

Andante (än-*dän*-tä). Moderately slow.

Andantino (än-dän-*tē*-nō). Faster than *Andante*.

Anima (*än*-ē-mä). Spirit; life.

Animando (än-ē-*män*-dō). With growing animation.

Animato (än-ē-*mä*-tō). In an animated style.

Assai (äs-*sä*-ē). Very.

Attacca (ät-*täk*-kä). Begin without pausing.

Barcarola (bär-kä-*rō*-lä). A Venetian boat song.

Ben (bĕn). Well.

Brillante (brēl-*län*-tĕ). Brilliant.

Brio (*brē*-ō). Spirit; vivacity.

Cantabile (kän-*tä*-bĕ-lä). In a singing style.

Coda (*kō*-dà). A few closing measures.

Col, colla, or *con* (kŏl, *kŏl*-lä, kŏn). With.

Commodo (*kŏm*-mō-dō). Leisurely; convenient.

Crescendo [*cresc.*] (krê-*shĕn*-dō). Gradually louder.

Da Capo [*D.C.*] (dä-*kä*-pō). From the beginning.

Dal Segno [*D.S.*] (däl-*sā*-nyō). From the sign :𝕊:.

Decrescendo (dā-krê-*shĕn* dō). Gradually softer.

Delicato (dêl-ē-*kä*-tō). Delicate.

Di (dē). Of.

Diminuendo [*dim.*] (dĭ-mĭn-ŭ-*ĕn*-dō). Gradually softer.

Dolce (*dōl*-tshä). Sweet.

E or *ed* (ā or äd). And.

Espressivo (ĕs-prĕs-*sē*-vō). With expression.

Fine (*fē*-nä). The end.

Forte [*f*] (*fôr*-tä). Loud.

Fortissimo [*ff*] (fôr-*tĭs*-ĭ-mō). Very loud.

Fuoco (fōō-ō-kō). Fire; energy.

Giocoso (jĭō-*kō*-sō). Playful.

Giojoso (jĭō-*yō*-sō). Joyful.

Giusto (*jŭ*-stō). Strict; precise.

Grandioso (grän-dē-*ō*-sō). Pompous; majestic.

Grazioso (grä-tsĕ-*ō*-sō). Gracefully.

Habanera (hä-bä-*nä*-rà), Spanish. A popular Havanese dance.

Largamente (lär-gä-*men*-tĕ). Broadly.

Larghetto (lär-*gĕt*-tō). Less slow than *Largo*.

Largo (*lär*-gō). Broad and slow.

Legato (lā-*gä*-tō). "Bound"; smoothly.

Leggiero (lĕd-*jä*-rō). Lightly.

Lento (*lĕn*-tō). Slow.

Ma (mä). But.

Maestoso (mä-ĕs-*tō*-sō). Majestic.

Marcato (mär-*kä*-tō). With emphasis.

Marcia (*mär*-chĕ-ä). A march.

Marziale (mär-tsē-*ä*-lĕ). In a martial manner.

Meno (*mā*-nō). Less.

Menuetto (mĕ-nōō-*ĕt*-tō). A minuet.

Mezzo [*m*] (*mĕd*-zo). Half; medium.

Moderato (mōd-ĕ-*rä*-tō). In moderate tempo.

Molto (*mōl*-tō). Much; very.

Mosso (*môs*-sō). Rapid.

Moto (*mō*-tō). Motion.

Non (nŏn). Not.

Pesante (pĕ-*sän*-tĕ). Heavy; ponderous.

Pianissimo [*pp*] (pē-ä-*nĭs*-ĭ-mō). Very soft.

Piano [*p*] (pē-*ä*-nō). Soft.

Piu (pyōō). More.

Poco a poco (*pō*-kō ä *pō*-kō). Little by little.

Presto (*prĕs*-tō). Very fast.

Primo (*prē*-mō). First.

Quasi (*kwä*-sē). Somewhat like; approaching.

Rallentando [*rall.*] (räl-lĕn-*tän*-dō). Gradually slower.

Risoluto (rĭ-sō-*lōō*-tō). Decided; energetic.

Ritardando [*rit.*] (rē-tär-*dän*-dō). Gradually slower.

Ritenuto [*riten.*] (rē-tĕ-*nōō*-tō). Gradually slower.

Rubato (rōō-*bä*-tō). "Robbed"; with varying tempo.

Scherzando (skĕr-*tsän*-dō). Playfully; with humor.

Semplice (sĕm-*plē*-tshĕ). Simple; unaffected.

Sempre (*sĕm*-prä). Always.

Senza (*sĕn*-tsä). Without.

Sforzando (sfôr-*tsän*-dō). Strongly accented.

Simile (*sē*-mĕ-lä). In the same manner.

Sostenuto (sōs-tä-*nōō*-tō). Sustained.

Staccato (stä-*kä*-tō). Detached; separated.

Tempo; a tempo (*tĕm*-pō). Time; in time.

Tenuto (tä-*nōō*-tō). Hold the full value.

Tranquillo (trän-*kwēl*-lō). In a quiet style.

Tremolo (*trä*-mō-lō). Reiterated rapidly.

Troppo (*trôp*-pō). Too much.

Tutti (*tōōt*-tē). All together.

Vigoroso (vē-gŏ-*rō*-sō). Energetic.

Vivace (vē-*vä*-tshĕ). In a spirited manner.

Voce (*vō*-tshĕ). The voice.

INDEX